Servi di Maria

University

aconi Casa

Sansedoni Palace

Salembini

The
Campo

Palazzo della Sigrioria

San Augustino

Porta

Tolomei

Podesla's

Palozzo del Capiteno

incasa's house

Baptistry

Santa Maria della Scala Ospeda

Duomo

Fonte Branda

Dominican Sisters
Hanford, Calif

✠

THE FLAME

Saint Catherine of Siena

✠

BUST OF SAINT CATHERINE

THE
FLAME

Saint Catherine of Siena

by

Jeanette Eaton

Author of
"A DAUGHTER OF THE SEINE"

Illustrated by
VICTOR PERARD

Harper & Brothers Publishers
NEW YORK AND LONDON

To
Florence Jeffrey Carlile

Acknowledgment

Grateful acknowledgment is hereby extended to Father Matthew L. Fortier, S.J., dean of the School of Sociology, and to Father Demetrius Zema, S.J., of the Department of History, Fordham University. Their generous assistance was invaluable not only in arranging those contacts in Rome and Siena essential to the preparation of this book, but in its critical examination before publication.

ILLUSTRATIONS

THE FLAME

Chapter One

WITH a rush of wings the swallows darted from the square brick belfry of San Domenico. Even before they reached the chestnut trees in the quiet little piazza below, the three great bells began to ring. Brief was their imperious, deep-toned clamour. Hardly had it ceased when softly across the gulch on that side of the town came the sweeter, mellower chime from the campanile of the cathedral.

To hear it evoked a sudden vision of white marble dome and tower, inlaid with delicate strips of black and touched with rose. Like the high treble in a mighty cantata the daring beauty of the Duomo soared above the more sombre notes rolled out by San Domenico, San Francesco, and by the great hospital and the Palazzo della Signoria, where sat the representatives of the Republic. Yet the voice of that

Republic was a blend of all these vast vibrations in stone. A composite of strange, rich, and clashing elements was the city of Siena in this year of 1353.

Now at the sound of the bells, women down by Fonte Branda, filling their bright copper pots under the shade of the lindens, paused and looked up. Watchmen at the city gates forgot for an instant the creaking carts drawn by white oxen lumbering out, and crossed themselves. Tradesmen in the shops and workmen at their benches stretched and sighed, knowing the long June afternoon was half done. Notaries laid down their quills. Fine ladies, working on tapestry beside tall windows in their palaces of brick and stone, yawned and wished their lords were not away fighting or hunting or conducting business.

From out his workshop, where apprentices were busy over steaming vats, Giacomo Benincasa strode into the hallway of his house. Wiping his hands on his leathern apron stained with blue and green and orange, he looked up the long stone staircase. At that moment he saw a stout figure pass across the terrace above.

"Lapa," he cried, "where is Caterina? Thrice have I called all through the house, but the child makes no answer."

Capped and covered with a triangle of brown linen tucked over her loose red frock, Mother Lapa paused on her way to the kitchen and sent a scornful glance downward.

"Truly I heard thy tongue make its din. What dost thou want of the child? Why hast thou left thy dye-pots before set of sun? Caterina has likely been snatched by a neighbour to while away the afternoon. They are always carrying her off. 'Monna Lapa,' they say to me, 'thou hast a child wise and sweet beyond her years. Your *bambina* of six has more sense than many a dame of sixty.' That's what they say of our little girl, my husband, and in some way thy favour is excused. But if thou dost expect me to watch her all day and attend to my cook-pots for the large family thou hast brought into the world, then thou canst think again!"

High and shrill the voice hurtled down. Violent gesticulations accompanied it. A stranger might have expected that, save for intervening space, the outburst would end with a smart cuff upon the ear. But Giacomo, after more than thirty years of marriage, knew those threatening palms meant no more than an escape of steam from his wife's boiler of energy. Humorously he clapped his hands over his ears. Then, placing his arms akimbo, he shook his head, laughing.

"Thy words are like an answer to the farmer's prayer. He asks for a little rain and receives a deluge." Turning on his wooden sandals, he passed into his dyeing shop.

Had the parents gone out to look up the steep street, they would have discovered the subject of their discussion. Not a stone's-throw away, sitting on the broad step of a tall house, little Catherine Benincasa was the centre of an absorbed group.

Her golden-brown head, now bent over a heap of flowers in her lap, now lifted to fling a laughing glance from soft dark eyes. While her fingers twisted the gay blossoms into a coronet she was telling a story about Saint Felix.

Four youngsters close beside her followed the tale with breathless interest. Not less quiet, altogether amused, three women completed the group. The two elders seated in the doorway were busy with sewing, and a young girl near them brushed white henna into her long black hair.

"And so," concluded Catherine, "just as the wolf was about to bite the sweet and holy man, Saint Felix filled his cheeks and puffed a great breath into the wolf's face and blew him into the sea, where he was drowned, and Saint Felix was safe from him forever." Her bright look of triumph circled the faces about her.

A burst of laughter came from the young woman hidden in the long strands of hair. "*Dio mio, cara,* what a breath that saint had! He must have eaten many leeks and onions before he saw the wolf!"

The comment drew cackles of appreciation from the elders in the doorway. But the story-teller's face grew sober.

"Truly, Maria," she said, reproachfully, "it wasn't *cipolle* that made his breath so strong. It was because he was pure and good."

Pushing back her hair, the girl bent upon the child an affectionate smile. "Ah, it is thou who art that, little Euphrosene. Thou art a saint thyself."

"Shh! Do not say such words!" Catherine sprang to her feet and her dark eyes lifted for an instant to the sailing white clouds overhead. "The saints are there." Then with a gentle smile she lifted the finished wreath and held it out to Maria. "You shall have my crown of flowers. Wear it when you go up to the church with your mother this evening, and perhaps your Tommaso will think you fairer than ever."

"Yes, yes," cried the other children, clapping their hands, "wear it for the *fidanzato*." And they laughed to see Maria's blushes.

At this moment a sturdy boy appeared in the street outside the Benincasa house. "Caterina!" he shouted, "the mother wishes thee!"

Instantly the child turned and waved. To the women in the doorway she murmured, "It is to see you again!" Then she sped down the hill with flying bare feet.

"We are to go to Fonte Branda and fetch water for supper," said the boy as she reached the door. "Go up and get thy pitcher from the kitchen."

"*Sì*, Stefano." Like a flash she leaped up the stone steps.

It was fun at any time to enter the kitchen. Something was always going on there over the great hearthstone where the soup kettle hung and the long loaves were baked. Strings of onions and apples swung from the dark cross-beams and lent their odours to the pungent aromas from the hearth.

"What a child art thou!" screamed Monna Lapa, whirling around as Catherine entered and waving a long wooden spoon. "Never at hand when wanted! Here, little vagabond, take this *brocca* and hasten to Fonte Branda! Otherwise thou wilt get no soup tonight. The pot is almost dry. Hurry, dost thou hear!"

Smiling in silence, the child took the pitcher from her mother's hands and held up her rosy face for the kiss she expected as the inevitable finish of her noisy parent's tirade.

In another moment Catherine and Stefano were pattering side by side down the slope to the fountain. This decline began far back in the town just off the main street and immediately fell steeply down straight to one of the city gates. On the lower slope lived the Benincasas so near the fountain that in the mornings Catherine could hear the women chattering and laughing over their laundry. She loved it down there under the trees; loved the pure spring which filled the great oblong basin of stone; loved the cold caress of the water when her hand plunged the jug through the placid surface.

It wasn't quite so much fun to carry the water back up the hill. She would have much preferred now to linger where men and women and a group of lads were gathered in the cool shade. But this was forbidden. Fonte Branda was one of the centres of the gossip and scandal in Siena and Monna Lapa knew right well that in half an hour enough evil things were said there—though all as a matter of joke and good humour—to darken a child's imagination forever. Catherine never dreamed of disobeying her mother's dictum. So beside Stefano she turned and trudged back with her burden.

This time the children went around the corner of the house to the side. For it was one of the fas-

THE WOMEN CHATTERING AND LAUGHING OVER THEIR LAUNDRY

cinating features of this building that, standing on a hillside as it did, it possessed a side door which opened on the second floor level right beside the kitchen. As they entered the door Giacomo Benincasa came out upon the terrace. He had divested himself of his work apron and, indeed, presented so comely and scrubbed an appearance in his doublet and tunic that Catherine guessed some plan was afoot.

"Where art thou going, my father, with thy cap on thy head?"

"Take in thy *brocca* and I'll tell thee." A moment later he was whispering to her softly: "Put on thy stockings, wash thy face and come with me. I must betake me across the town and I'd like thy company."

Gleefully she ran to get ready. And soon she was trotting along beside her father up the hill toward the winding street which, with several changes of name, wound like a snake through the main portions of the city. Siena was divided into three parts or *terzas* and these, into smaller units called *contrade*. Each had its emblem and in festival time and at the games and jousting matches men carried banners on which the emblems were painted. The Benincasas lived in the *contrada* of the Goose. Now Catherine and her father were passing through the *contrada* of the Dragon.

"Where do we go, father?"

"To Messer Currado Maconi's house to plan an order for the dyeing of his stuffs."

To the child the name meant nothing. But it had

sounded on the good dyer's lips with pardonable pride. Although not of the highest nobility, the Maconi family was an important one and occupied a great brick house with a mighty Gothic tower. Servants, horses, men-at-arms and all the signs of wealth and honour belonged to Messer Currado. To do business with him was for Benincasa more than mere profit. It was a pleasure. For he and the signore always talked a bit of the wars and the taxes and the latest changes in the government.

Catherine's bright dark eyes were noting everything along the way. At first the pedestrians were Dominican Brothers. In their white habits and black cloaks, they were hastening back to the convent perched on the hill of Camporeggi crowning the slope where Catherine lived. For her to see them was to feel rise within her an overpowering sense of gratitude and love for these earnest preachers of the way of God. Even after they had passed by, the child turned back to bless them with a final glance.

"Beware there, *per Dio!*"

The harsh cry and an abrupt clatter of hoofs on the paving stones made Catherine swerve aside almost from under the prancing feet of a great grey horse. Safe against the wall of a house, with her father beside her, she glanced curiously upward at the scowling face of the rider. She had an impression of his youth and of his striking costume of blue and orange.

"Canst thou not look out for thy betters, *bambina?*" the horseman cried imperiously.

From Giacomo's lips came a dignified protest.

"Young sir, you should not be galloping through the streets so hastily. You had better lead your horse. Are the Malavolti fighting again?"

The young cavalier—he could hardly have been thirteen—looked down at the speaker to determine whether he was joking. With disdainful candour he replied, "I am not yet of an age to fight, but when I am let enemies of the Malavolti have a care!"

With that he wheeled his horse to the left and rode him into a great doorway across the street. In the dark courtyard within Catherine could see him dismount.

Close together here where the street curved dwelt three great families of Siena. The vast palace of the Malavolti elbowed the vaster palace of the Salimbeni—each with its tall blind tower of grey stone. Across the way, frowning defiantly stood the habitation of the Tolomei. The formidable stones of this fortress were lighted at the second story by five great Gothic windows decorated with lacy carvings and divided by slender stone pillars. Glancing up, Catherine beheld leaning from one aperture a lady in a dark red robe fastened with gold buttons. Even as she looked the lovely face smiled and a white hand tossed a rose to some one in the street.

Quickly as the child glanced about, however, it was impossible to see who had caught the flower. There were too many gentlemen and horses and tradesmen and beggars all milling about from one place to another. Clinging tightly to her father's hand, she pushed with him through the press.

Shouts, tradesmen's cries, snatches of muttered conversation, greetings and commands filled her ears with sociable din. The sunshine of late afternoon fell upon gay cloaks and gleaming hilts of daggers, lit up the sombre, bearded face of a Franciscan monk in his brown habit, made a ruby pool of the scarlet robe worn by some learned doctor walking slowly homeward from the University.

Presently they came to a tiny dark street so narrow and steep it was like a staircase without steps. Right under a tall house it dived and when they came out of it Catherine looked about her in amazement. Here was an enormous open place surrounded with great palaces of rosy brick gleaming in the sun. Sloping gently downward from where she stood and sweeping in a great curve left and right, the piazza had exactly the shape of a fluted shell. Opposite her stood a beautiful building with delicately pillared windows all across and under them the black and white escutchions of the Republic. Beside it, flying up and up into the blue sky, with a belfry like a crown, stood a slender tower of incredible height. The arrowy beauty of its leap made her catch her breath in wonder.

"Hast thou never seen the Campo, Caterina?" asked her father smiling down at her. "Over there is the Palazzo della Signoria where sit the Nine who govern us and that is the tower where sounds the bell when the enemy is at the gates. Here is held the market. Here the games take place. In the Campo everything happens. It is the heart of Siena."

Over the pale pink paving bricks between which grass blades pushed hopefully they walked on. The Campo seethed with life. Urchins played about the Fonte Gaia. Housewives were making late purchases at the stalls. Groups of citizens stood in excitable chatter. Presently they left the glory of the piazza, passed between two grave palaces and were at the gate of the Maconi mansion. The moment they were within its cool courtyard the noise and confusion of the streets were hushed.

A servant led them into a roofed inner court. Here, with flowers growing all about the paved space, it was light and cheerful. "Sit you down," said the servant and pointed to a stone bench. "I shall call the master."

He came soon enough down the staircase from the upper apartments—a tall gentleman, stately in his green, skirted doublet. Beside him, stretching his short legs to match his father's steps, came a little boy. The moment his foot touched the flagstones of the court he stood stock-still, his eyes fixed on Catherine.

"Good day, Giacomo Benincasa," said the master of the house. Then, bestowing a pat on Catherine's sunny brown head, he asked, "Is this the youngest of thy family—*ecco*, how many children didst thou say?"

"Twenty-five in all, Messer Currado," replied Benincasa proudly. "But, alas, hardly half that number are alive today."

"Even so, a goodly brood to raise! It is well thou

art so prosperous a fellow. And when was this *bambina* born?"

"The year before the plague, Messer Currado. A marvel how so young a babe lived through that fearful time."

"So? Then she is exactly the age of my son, Stefano, there." He waved his hand and smiled back at the boy. "Wouldst thou believe it? Already he learns to sit a horse."

Catherine looked with shy pleasure at this marvel of precocity. She wished she had a flower to give him. Swiftly her eyes wandered from his silken hose and velvet doublet to his dark curls and smiling red lips. If he would only speak! But just as she took a step in his direction Messer Currado turned and told him sternly to run at once to his mother. The boy flung a laughing glance at Catherine and promptly scampered off.

She sighed to see him go. Soon, amidst all the talk about the wools and silk stuffs to be dyed and the coming and going of servants with rolls of goods for her father to finger and consider, the little girl began to feel sleepy. Such an everlasting flow of words!

What she was next conscious of was her father taking from the pouch at his belt a sheaf of parchment. "Had you the goodness, Messer Currado," said he hesitatingly, "I would think it a favour were you to read me a bit of this script. I have it as a loan from one Angelo Turae, a friend of a man with whom I do business. It seems he wrote this down after the plague to keep fresh in mind that terrible visitation of God. Some say it is well done and I should like to know."

Curiously Maconi took the parchments. Spreading them out, he seated himself and presently with nod of head began to read.

"And I, Angelo Turae, called Graffo, buried my five children in one ditch with my own hands and so did many other families."

The reader paused to cross himself, skipped a portion and read on.

"The bells did not sound nor did anyone weep—even those who would have liked to do so—for almost every person expected his own death. And in this way things were going people did not believe that anyone would survive and many men believed and said this is the end of the world."

"Santa Maria!" cried Giacomo, "he writes the truth. It was like that. There were not enough priests to say Mass for the dying. Corpses lay in the street. Do you remember? Not a house but had its dead. Whole families wiped out! Ah, our fair Siena has not recovered yet from the blow."

"Nor ever will, I fear," replied Maconi gravely. "Four times as many persons died as there were left to mourn. Hundreds of houses stand empty still in our city and trade has hardly begun to mend. But let me read on a bit to what came after the Black Death.

"The people who escaped death all made merry and thought of nothing but of rejoicing and took no heed of spending and entertaining. Each man appeared to be rich merely because he was alive and that he had escaped the pestilence. And all those who remained were as if they had been brothers. One recognized the other and every man made himself as if he was related and gave feasts and everyone seemed to be rejoicing in the world."

Slowly Maconi shifted the parchments, glancing here and there. His face was sad. "*Si*, it is well put. That was a time of madness. It had to pass. But what a pity the feeling that men were brothers had to pass with it. There is as much contention here as ever. And I fear that men like thee, Giacomo, men in trade who now control the government, will not be able to keep the peace." He rose to his feet and the two men sounded each other's eyes.

Catherine had no idea what the last words meant. Yet she felt that the gentleman had changed all at once. An instant before he had been like a friend. Now he was the lord of a great brick palace speaking to a person of small importance. She slipped her hand into her father's and copied his bow as he asked leave to go. She was glad then when a smile came once more into the tall man's eyes.

As if to atone for his hauteur of a moment before, he said gently: "Thou must be careful, Giacomo, of a little child with such wise eyes. She must not understand too much of this wicked world."

It was almost dusk when the two reached home once more. The family, gathered in the kitchen for supper, were already seated at the long table. Candles in iron holders aided the bright fire on the hearth to light the room. The smell of spices and warm bread mingled with the great clatter of tongues and the scolding welcome of Mother Lapa. Wearily little Catherine sank on the bench beside Stefano and almost before she had eaten her soup her head was nodding.

Next morning at her prayers she suddenly remembered the dream she had had. Curled up in the big bed between her two sisters, she had dreamed of people dancing over graves and weeping. Then an angel came to comfort them and everyone knelt while the cathedral bell began to ring. She was still wondering about this dream while she was peeling carrots for her mother out on the cool terrace. And she saw with delight coming up the stairs the white-robed figure of Tommaso della Fonte. He was the very one to tell her what it meant.

As long as Catherine could remember this grave young man had been a member of the household. She knew that her father had adopted him because he had been orphaned in the plague five years ago. And now he was a novice of the Dominican Order of friars up at Camporeggi. How often he had told her of his studies and recited marvellous stories of the Saint who founded the order more than a hundred years ago. It was to Tommaso rather than to anyone else that the child took her troubles and her questions.

Today, however, the young man made light of her inquiry. "Who knows where dreams come from?" he asked smiling and playfully snatched a bit of peeled carrot from the wooden bowl. Then he added more gravely: "If thou wert ever to have a real vision, child, thou wouldst not mistake it for a dream. My slumbers were filled with terrible pictures for twelve months after the pestilence, but they were meaningless. In prayer there is always healing for the mind."

These words of della Fonte were to come back to little Catherine a few weeks later. She and Stefano had gone to take noonday dinner with their elder sister Bonaventura. Since her marriage she lived in the oldest and highest part of Siena beyond the Duomo.

On the way back the children came along the Fosse di San Ansano, named for the first Christian of Siena, martyred in old Roman days. The route took them along the mighty walls of the great hospital, Santa Maria della Scala, and gave them a view of the charming country to the west. Far away, the undulating hills of Chianti were insubstantial shadows. Nearby those hollows and depressions, so strangely scooped out here and there within the city, were filled with olive orchards gleaming silver grey in the bright sunshine.

From the Fosse they had to enter the narrow lane of Vallepiata. Stefano quicked his pace. He knew the villainous reputation of this neighbourhood. Indeed, not long since the Signoria had declared by statute that the passage should be closed at night because, "Very dark it is of evenings and there are done in that place many vile, unhonest deeds and cut-throats lie in wait there to assault and slay people." True, by day it was only dirty and crowded. But the boy was glad when they were nearly at the end.

"Now," he said, "at this next turn we can see Camporeggi and San Domenico. Look!"

There it was—the vast sheer height of brick topped by the square, crenellated belfry. Above the red-tiled roofs and garden walls the church rose powerful in the simple grandeur of its soaring lines. It seemed the very embodiment of austere dedication. To Stefano the sight of it meant merely that he was nearing home and he hurried through the crowds of gossiping women and shouting gamins in the street.

Presently he realized that his little sister was not beside him. He looked back and then impatiently retraced his steps. "What is the matter? At what dost thou stare? I see nothing."

Unaware of his question as of the jostling people, Catherine was standing like a small figure of wood. Her head was lifted toward the sky and her wide-open eyes were blank and blind. Yet a look of bliss such as Stefano had never seen—not even when Bonaventura kissed her baby—rested on her face. It held him an instant in silence.

For Catherine the skies above San Domenico had seemed to open. Strange and marvellous shapes, a blend of colours more glorious than Duccio had painted in his "Maestas" at the Duomo floated there within the blue. What could it be? Rapture drowned her heart and it seemed as if suddenly she had left her little body in the lane and were caught up there in the iridescent world behind the world.

"What dost thou see, Caterina? Come! Canst

thou not hear?" Frightened now, Stefano shook his sister by the arm.

Back came the dark eyes to life and flashed on him a dazzled beam of happiness before they turned to look upwards again. Then a cry started from her lips. "It is gone! Oh, wicked Stefano, to make it go!" Burying her face in her chubby hands, the child began to weep.

In vain Stefano tried to comfort her. In vain, embarrassed by the stares of passers-by, he scolded and cajoled. At last, with a bitter sigh, Catherine took an uncertain step forward and in silence the two trudged down to the via Galluzza and thus home.

Days passed before anyone noticed that something had happened to Catherine. Then Monna Lapa, like a worried bee, buzzed misgivings through the house. The child did not look well. She was droopy and silent—she who was by nature a sunbeam. Shouldn't she have a dose of herbs? Somebody must find out where she felt distress. Then it was—in the midst of the fussing—that Stefano told of his sister's strange behaviour on the way from Bonaventura's house. Instantly, like a flock of birds, the questions and demands settled down upon Catherine.

Harried and puzzled, she tried to explain. "I saw —I saw over Camporeggi ——" Oh, how could she put it into words? She bent an anguished look upon her father's kind face. "Only it wasn't just the sky—it was—was Heaven and they were blessing me. I wanted to stay there—I didn't want it to fade away and so I cried."

"Who was blessing thee, *cara*?" asked her father gently.

"The Lord," she murmured. "Oh, it was real and true!" she touched his sturdy arm, "realer than thou art. It was as Tommaso said, no dream. And I want—oh, I want to belong—to be part of it again."

Her parents could make nothing of such broken bits. They gave her hot drinks of bitter herbs. They bade her run out in the sun and air. They tried to distract her with a hundred small tasks and errands. But month followed month and still the child kept her absorbed quietness. Still she made it plain that what she wanted above all else was to be alone. They would find her hiding away in some dark recess of the big house. They would see her going up the stone stairway on her knees, telling her rosary. Her brothers jeered. Her parents shook their heads and scolded. No one understood.

Once she left home for good and all. With a small loaf of bread filched from her mother's cupboard, she made off along the edge of Fontebranda and out the gate of San Sano. It was the first time she had ever been outside the city walls. She turned her head this way and that to see if she could discover any of the robber bands they talked of at her father's table. Wicked men they were who carried off the peasants' pigs and burned their houses. But all she heard was the sound of horns from a party of huntsmen.

Before she had gone far, she found what she was looking for. It was a sort of hollow between rocks and trees. This would be her cave. Like the Saints of the desert, she would now become a hermit and live in prayer and fasting. She began this program by devouring hungrily the crisp loaf of bread. Then she said her prayers. Surely here in the quiet and peace she would be able to see it again—that real world where dwelt Jesus and the Saints! She tried to think again what it was like. Suddenly the sound of the grasshopper's uneasy song and the shine of the leaves in the sun disappeared from sight and hearing. It came again, that vision to fill her heart with joy. It was as if her body slept there in the hollow and she herself rose to some dizzy height where she knew a strange blend of fear and rapture. Gradually she floated down again and almost before she could turn her face to the warm earth she was asleep.

Waking, she forgot everything except that she was far from home. The sun was low. Softly in the distance she heard the vesper bell of San Domenico. What if the city gates were locked and she outside in the chill of night? Swiftly the little hermit scrambled to her feet and scampered up the hill.

Catherine fully expected a terrific tirade from her mother. But for once it did not come. Her waiting ears told her that a topic of vaster interest occupied the household. Through chinks of rapid talk she caught a glimpse of what had been happening in the city that day. A visit from the Emperor Carlo—who was he? She heard her brothers speak of trains of soldiers and cavalcades of knights. She wished they would tell of their horses and their fine garments. But the talk had changed and was all about fighting in the Campo.

"They took the treasure box from the church on Camporeggi," shouted Bartolommeo. "I saw them dragging it tied to the tail of an ass. And there was a great shout, 'Death to the Nine!' They called them traitors, robbers, thieves, and anyone who could think of any other evil name said it. With my own eyes I saw one of the magistrates struck down with a poignard and men fleeing in all directions."

Catherine heard her father's voice ring out from the end of the table. "They make the coming of the Emperor the reason for the overthrow of the government. But will a better one be set in its place? Meanwhile Carlo will have his fill of gold florins, never fear!"

Benincasa rose from his place. Munching that favourite pastry called *panforte* which is made in Siena to this day, he strolled over to the hearthstone where Catherine perched on her low stool. "Well, *bambina*," he said absently, "it is all one to thee whether the Nine fall or not, I see."

Yes, thanks to Emperor Charles Fourth and the turbulence his entry caused, little Catherine Benincasa went to bed without being reproached for fleeing to the desert. Yet a year or two later an even greater uproar in the town would not have disguised her absence from the house for an hour. With the approach of girlhood the whole character of her life was caused to change.

Faced by the problem of this strange child, Lapa had one sure comfort. It was the reflection that when she was old enough to be married all would be well. And that was not far off, for in those days girls married at fifteen, or even at an earlier age. For the wife of Benincasa to reflect was, of course, to speak. And from her eleventh year on Catherine heard little else about herself than talk of the time when a husband would be chosen for her.

At first she paid no heed. She was absorbed in responding to the mighty urge upon her—resistless as the tide upon the sea—to live in that vision of oneness with the Spirit. Instinctively she began a battle with physical gratifications which was to last for years. She refused to eat meat. Quietly she slipped her portion to Stefano's plate or tossed it to the cats under the table. She kept herself awake at night and rose early in the morning for meditation. She tried to learn every week something new from Tommaso della Fonte about the teachings of Christ. Slowly, however, it dawned on her that she was expected to have an altogether different preoccupation.

The word marriage sounded abstract enough on her mother's lips. But the small girls in the Quarter of the Goose gave it substance. Already they were saying to one another, "May the husband my parents find for me be rich and handsome!" or "God send me a husband whose kisses are warm as the sun!"

Such images flung on the screen of Catherine's mind filled her with rebellion. They threatened what she had striven to place within her heart—one single ideal of Goodness. When the rough young apprentices came singing and joking out of her father's shop, when she watched them wipe their mouths wet with wine upon the backs of their hands, when she saw them exchanging a wink as they regarded her small person, she ran away trembling and revolted. What if she were to be possessed and commanded by a man such as these? Ever since childhood she had said to herself that she would never marry, but would keep a single heart for God. Now every day made her more certain of her vow.

Whenever she caught her small daughter fleeing from sight of the apprentices, Lapa would laugh and say, "Child, they are not serpents!"

No, Catherine thought to herself, but they represented a deadly danger. In amazement she watched her playmates submit joyously to their fate. Overnight they turned into women. They put on pretty clothes, assumed coquettish ways, spent hours arranging their hair and took up housewifery arts. That was the sum of feminine education in those days. Only children of the rich—and at that very seldom girls—were taught to read and write.

Catherine herself liked learning to make bread and pasties and to wash the clothes. She loved the busy days at her father's small farm in the country. What struck her to the heart was her loss of freedom. Now she could go nowhere unattended—not even up the hill to San Domenico. In vain she protested silently or in passionate phrases of revolt. Her elders only smiled and said that marriage was her destiny and this narrow path the way to it. What on earth was she thinking of?

"Of serving God," she would answer.

Bonaventura tried persuasion. Once when Catherine was about fourteen, the elder sister made a lovely robe for her of blue silk with gold embroidery about the neck. Proudly she showed it to the strange girl.

"Now," said Bonaventura cajolingly, "do not be an ungrateful *ragazza*. This thou must wear to the ball my friends are giving in the Terza di Città."

Catherine looked ready to cry. But she hated to hurt her sister and so she let herself be arrayed for the occasion. First they combed out the lovely chestnut tresses in the sun to bleach, perfumed her with unguents and rouged her cheeks and lips. When she was dressed Monna Lapa and her sensible daughters cried out with delight.

"Now thou art lovely," they said, "it will not be hard to find a *fidanzato* for thee."

Lying awake at dawn and listening to the matin bells, Catherine wondered how good people like her mother and sisters could bear these foolish artifices. How could anybody think them important? As for her, what she wanted was utterly different. Life and more life! Not mockeries! Ah, she knew there was but one stream of living water without which the soul perishes. To kneel in the dusky tranquillity of San Domenico was to see held aloft one single image of perfection. A lifetime was short enough to try to reach up to Him. Why did those who loved her not see that to follow that Example was what real living meant?

In her sixteenth year she had a brief period of peace, a sorrowful peace. For the devoted Bonaventura died. In her grief Catherine was let alone by others who were mourning, too. Yet before the year was out the menace confronting her became definite. One day the girl entered the kitchen unexpectedly and found Lapa talking with a neighbour.

"A good family, a fine match!" Catherine heard her say. "Giacomo and I find Luigi well established as a worker in metals and believe he will make our Caterina an excellent husband."

In terror the girl fled away to Stefano's room. Crouching in its darkest corner, she said to herself: "It is come! It is upon me! The very name of the proposed husband has been pronounced!" This time there could be no postponement. She must announce her vow publicly and at once.

That evening in a fury of excitement, Catherine sought her parents out. "You must go no further in the matter you have at heart!" she panted. "I have taken to myself a vow and this I shall not break. I will *not* be married! Never! No!"

Angry and discountenanced as they were, Monna Lapa and her husband still refused to take her seriously. They thought her outbreak some unique form of youthful rebellion. Hopefully they consulted Tommaso della Fonte. He had been taken into the Dominican Order now and was called Father. The young man laughed uncomfortably when confronted with the task of advising the strange girl. But he promised to see what he could do.

One morning he knocked on Catherine's door. He found her walking up and down in great agitation. Seating himself on the wooden bench, he questioned her closely. She surprised him by the finality of her determination. Despite her emotion, it was clear that here was no adolescent vagary. She meant it!

"Well, if thou wilt not marry," he said thoughtfully, "thou must be a nun and I shall try to help thee in that vocation."

The small figure stopped before him. The dark eyes tried to say what lay in her heart. "But—no— I do not wish to be a nun!" With intense earnestness she added: "There are other ways to serve God. I will find them."

Father della Fonte had never heard of such a thing. There was no middle course for girls in the fourteenth century. "But ——" he stammered. "How canst thou stay at home and be an old maid? Thou wilt be laughed at. Thy parents will never be reconciled."

"Oh, if they would only let me alone!" she cried out through clenched teeth. "It would matter not who laughed. I—I know how to learn—how to find my way. Help me, oh, help me! What will put an end to these marriage plans?"

Della Fonte pondered. He was half convinced. From earliest childhood this girl had shown a heart bent in one direction. Strange she should refuse to enter a nunnery. But perhaps she had been shown another way.

"Cut off thy hair!" he said suddenly. "No maiden with shorn locks could possibly be betrothed." Then he rose to go. The light he had kindled in Catherine's eyes frightened him.

Even before he had reached the bottom of the staircase the savage snip of scissors was sounding in the room above. Off came the beautiful thick tresses and fell in jagged masses to the floor. As she finished the ruin the girl's face was flushed with triumph. "For liberty!" she murmured.

Then, staring at the bright heap at her feet, she felt a pang shoot through her heart. Somehow she knew it was her youth lying there, cut off before its time. Yes, it was true, but what did it matter? A new life awaited her now.

Chapter Two

UP THE via Stalloreggi from the Laterina gate one September day two young men rode back into Siena. Their peaked caps, the horns slung across their tunics revealed the fact that their return was from the hunt. Passers-by smiled to see them and small urchins shouted, "What luck?"

The elder of the two riders, pleased by the admiration in those grimy little faces, pointed to the string of partridge and wild geese around his saddle bow. Then he cried, "The others bring a boar and rabbits. Watch and see!"

As he spoke, he raised one gloved hand to stroke the capped falcon on his shoulder. "The best of peregrines, this!" he said to his companion. "When she stoops upon her quarry there is no escape for it. She is like some fair ladies that I know, Stefano!" Merry and careless, his blue eyes turned to the boy beside him.

Stefano Maconi was the very individual Catherine Benincasa had seen in his father's house ten years before. He had been shy then in the presence of the dyer's small daughter. And even now his frank boyish face, fixed so admiringly upon his companion, held a hint of the same diffidence. Yet his glance said plainly that he would like nothing so well as to grow up to rival the bold horsemanship and noble bearing of Francesco Malavolti.

The latter was five years the elder of the two and at twenty-one was already deeply versed in the ways of the world. Yet because his family was on warm terms of friendship with the Maconi, Francesco occasionally condescended to take this sixteen-year-old with him to the hunt. Moreover, he found it rather fun by tales and hints to open those innocent eyes. It was time Stefano took part in a few of the mad escapades for which all Sienese bloods were noted in 1363.

Walking their horses now, they came to the intersection of a street. It led to the palace of the Captain of the People near the cathedral. Pointing to a slender arch of stone flung across the street from one Gothic house to another, Francesco said, "If it had not been for that bridge it would have gone hard with me the other night."

"Were you out after curfew?" asked Stefano.

The other nodded with mature contempt for the

bell which sent only the timid home. "Truly I was. With a friend I was serenading sweet Madonna Margherita whose husband is in Champagne buying carpets. While we sang she came to the window and motioned that she would let us in. At once things began to happen. First her father appeared and hurled out a great brass pitcher full of water. We dodged and it struck a great fellow passing by in the darkness. He howled that he was being set upon and another came running with a shout. Heads popped out of windows. Women screamed. And two men at arms hastened from Il Capitano's palace. The door opened under madonna's hand just in time to save us. We ran up the stairs, climbed out her bedroom window and hastened across that bridge. Over three roofs we scrambled and then were safe at my friend's house. *Dio mio,* what a narrow escape!"

Both young men were still laughing when they reached the turn leading to the Maconi house. But Francesco laid a hand upon his friend's knee. "Come with me to dine at home. Young Ranieri di Landoccio of the Pagliaresi family is here and waits for me at my house. I think he would like to see you."

"Neri makes his studies at Perugia, I hear," said Stefano. "I would I might travel like that and see the world. My parents scarcely permit me out the city gates." He turned his horse beside Francesco's. "Yes, I will dine with you gladly."

In a few moments they had entered the courtyard of the Malavolti palace. It was here that little Catherine had seen dismount the haughty boy who had nearly run her down. And, indeed, Francesco was he. His manner was still disdainful enough toward the "Little People," as the tradesmen and the poor were called. But with his friends he was charming.

Now he conducted his visitor up the stairway and into a great room with cross beams painted in brilliant designs. Costly rugs lay on the stone floor and, since already the heavy curtains were drawn across the windows, candles flamed in sconces all about the walls. Beside the bright fire sat a lady. She was embroidering a pair of knitted gloves and at her feet lay a small white dog.

"The hunt went well, mother." Francesco stooped and kissed the lady's cheek. "I sent a page with the spoils to the kitchen. And here is some one come to help eat them."

The lady held out a white hand which Stefano kissed with a low bow. "How fares your good mother, Madonna Giovanna?" she asked.

When Stefano had replied Francesco took him at once into his bedroom. There on a cushioned bench beside the canopied bed sat a youth little older than Stefano. By the light of a tall candle holder, his slender hands grasping the sides of an iron reading stand, he was poring over a manuscript. As the others entered he sprang up with a gracious smile.

"Greetings, Neri di Landoccio," cried his host and clasped his hand. "This is Stefano Maconi whose house stands so near your own." He waited an instant for the two to exchange courtesies and then said curiously, "What are you reading there? You are like a mouse with cheese when you find a book."

Neri laughed pleasantly and his eyes lighted. "It is a copy but lately made in Florence of Dante's *Purgatorio*."

"Oh, that thunderer!" cried Francesco. "I would rather listen to your own poems or the *sonetti* of Folgore of San Geminiano. Come, repeat for us one of his verses—the one about the hunt."

Stefano sat down in a high-backed chair to listen. Throwing back his dark head, Neri said, "The one called 'Saturday' it is. Listen then." In a voice full of dramatic emphasis he began to recite.

> "On Saturday men's pleasure and delight
> Is to hunt birds with the falcon
> That strikes down crane and heron
> Rising and falling at dizzy height.
>
> "And fiercely smites wild geese, tearing
> Until they lose their wings, legs and rumps.
> Chargers and palfreys are put to spur
> And men shout for glory and for daring.
>
> "Then back home! Tell Cook to take the lot,
> Save the skins for tomorrow's tanning
> And place all, plucked and ready, in the pot.
>
> "And have white bread and wines so rare
> That all will seem joyous and festive
> Thus never will the board be bare!"

Francesco clapped his friend on the shoulder. "Well spoken, truly! What could be better than that verse?"

"Or more suited to the day we have just spent?" chimed in Stefano in delight.

"*Si, si!* And we must make ready for the feasting, friends. Wash your hands and face here at this basin, Stefano. In another poem Folgore speaks of the pleasure of cold water on the skin."

The next hour before dinner was served they spent pleasantly in the great room. Francesco's mother asked Neri about his studies in Perugia. He replied eagerly. Then to make the talk more general he asked if they had heard here as in Perugia that the new Pope, Urban Fifth, was rousing himself against the foreign bands of marauders in the country.

"Yes," replied Francesco, "and he has need. After the freebooters defeated the last Pope's own troops near Avignon and compelled him to pay a heavy ransom, they are worse than ever. We of Siena have done better—thanks to Ceccolo of the Orsini. For once we completely routed the Company of the Hat this year. They say Lippo di Vanni is going to make a painting of the victory for the Palazzo della Signoria."

"But," said Neri, "there are other wandering bands. That English villain, John Hawkwood, is absolutely fearless and his White Company has been raging over the countryside for years. No road is safe anywhere and what the peasants suffer is terrible. It seems strange the fighting men of the Republics in Italy cannot put an end to the curse."

Francesco rose from the window-seat and stretched. "Oh, well, who wants to fight those ruf-

fians? There is fighting enough here for the honour
of one's own house. For me, I'd rather hunt. What
say you, Stefano?"

The boyish face reddened under the attention
fixed upon him. He had politely followed all that
Neri said, but felt no part in it. The feuds of Siena,
however, lay close to his heart. "It is my great
hope," said he shyly, "soon to help my father in all
his endeavours for the Maconi."

"Well spoken, young sir!" boomed a deep voice.
Francesco's father had entered the room and stood
smiling at the group. In a doublet with slashed
sleeves, long silk hose, a fine white shirt which
showed at the throat, he was a most elegant gentleman. He bowed low over his wife's hand. Raising
his head he added with a significant gesture, "To
hold the Tolomei in place is, indeed, labour enough
for the rest of us. But come, let us go in to dinner."

Along the tapestried walls of the dining-room
servants waited with steaming platters. The bare
board was strewn with fine dishes, crystal goblets,
pitchers of faïence. Candles in holders made in the
shape of animals shed a glow upon the tray of fruit
in the centre. At each place was a spoon of hammered silver. This was for vegetables and sauces.
But the meat was torn apart in the fingers which
were then dipped in a bowl of crystal and wiped
upon a napkin.

At table they discussed the hunt. Then Francesco
began to tease his parents by asking facetiously if
they had settled yet upon his future bride. To stop
his tongue his mother inquired of Neri if he had

leanings to enter some Order of the Church. And wistfully the boy replied that he had read too many books from Greece and ancient Rome for sufficient singleness of faith.

"Ah, that should not stop you," cried Malavolti senior, "most of the cultured men are among the clergy. Look at Father Lazzarino of Pisa who lectures at our University. His collection of books is unrivalled. He is a philosopher. So might you be."

Neri's sensitive face flushed painfully. "No, I could not be like that. It seems unhonest I should have to have faith."

"Oh, he is a poet," laughed Francesco. "Doubtless he thinks only of *bell'amore* or a *bella donna*."

At a signal from their hostess the others arose and followed the whisper of her silken robe into the great hall. As the three young men stood about the fireplace they seemed in their grace and high spirits the very flower of their time and country—the debonair blade, the scholar-poet, the soldierly gallant. And now, as if to complete the one element lacking in the group, they were joined by the artist. Escorted by a servant, bowing in the doorway, stood Andrea Vanni. In his middle twenties this man was a familiar figure in the social life of Siena. Interested in every form of life, a dabbler in the politics of the day, he yet had the dreamy eyes of the painter, the quiet observation of a thoroughly detached individual.

Neri felt an instant sympathy for him. While Stefano, Francesco and Malavolti sat talking of wars and family hatreds, the other two young men

eagerly exchanged opinions. Andrea, who knew
Perugia, spoke warmly of the buildings and public
fountain there. And they discussed their own city
and mutually wondered whether with the general
shortage of funds the new cathedral, that vast
dream in stone, would ever be built around the old.

"Siena was so great, so powerful a hundred years
ago," said Andrea sadly, "and now it is full of strife
and littleness. Sometimes I think, did some one great
being rise amongst us we would feel a change of
heart. We have no leaders."

"Do you mean some statesman?" asked Neri. He
said it without much interest, for he thought politics very tiresome. But Vanni's answer surprised
him.

"No," he said slowly, his visionary eyes fixed on
the flaming logs, "I think it would be some one who
could give nourishment to the soul's life. We grow
too far from God. The Church becomes worldly
since the Pope remains at Avignon and we are sheep
without a shepherd." He nodded toward Francesco.
"*Ecco!* That young man, for example! He thinks
of nothing but pleasure. They all do that—pleasure
and battle! Nobleness comes not to a city when the
young dream no dreams of great things."

Vanni might have said this, not of his own city
alone, but of all Italy. The fourteenth century was
a time of confusion and strife. Inevitably so. Since
the breaking up of the old Roman Empire the country had never been united. The Popes had had a
vision of unity. Charlemagne had vaguely achieved
it as part of his European empire. But never after-

wards was there an Emperor who mastered the tendency of each country to develop its nationality. As for the Pope, his temporal power was contested bitterly by ambitious princes both within and without Italy. And now in his absence from Italy, that kingless country had no leadership whatsoever.

What had happened during the Middle Ages was the development in Italy of free cities. Each one was a little, separate Republic. Since every city wished to be supreme there was constant war. Venice battled with Genoa and Genoa with Pisa for the rule of the sea. Florence fought with Siena, Perugia and Assisi. Milan conquered in the north. Leagues between towns for the purpose of conquest or protection were made and broken continually.

Moreover, within the cities themselves all was contention. The nobles and the rich strove with tradesmen and the poor for control of the government. And whenever either a city or a party got worsted it demanded that the Pope or the so-called Emperor would send them aid. The Guelf party of the Pope struggled against the Ghibelline party of the Emperor. But seldom did city, party or even individual remain consistently loyal to either power.

Few people at that time understood the real cause of all this conflict. As a matter of fact, all the people of Europe were emerging from the Middle Ages. Men were forced by changed conditions to fix their attention more keenly than before upon the physical world. They were busy making new things, improving living conditions, inventing novel methods of work. Trade, banking, commerce began to boom.

And all this took place because new conditions begot a new element in the consciousness of man. This was individualism. Men began to feel within themselves the ego or I as never before. Upon the vast majority the effect of this dawning power was to inspire a ruthless passion for personal success.

Andrea Vanni might have gone on with his analysis of the young men gathered in the Malavolti palace that evening. If Francesco desired power over the hearts of women, Stefano Maconi longed no less for social power won by means of the force of arms. Even Neri di Landoccio, sensitive and aspiring as he was, represented the wish for power of the intellect. They were young egoists all. And their elders offered no better example of unselfishness. None of them cared deeply for the good of Siena. They never gave a thought to the welfare of Italy as a whole or of the great Church of Christendom.

As the guests rose to take leave of their hosts this dominant note of self-interest rose frankly to the surface. It was evoked by Malavolti. Looking about the circle of faces, he said: "A pity it is that none amongst you young men has entered the Church. Do you not know what power would be yours as Archbishops and Cardinals?"

"Yes," cried his son Francesco in cynical amusement, "one would give up nothing and gain much."

"Not for me," said Stefano quickly. "I could not then bear arms."

When the three guests reached the street Andrea Vanni waited until the young Maconi had ridden off. Then, clasping Neri's hand, he said, "And what of you? Have you thought of the magnificent books you could have were you made a Cardinal?"

Looking into those mocking eyes, Neri blushed. "You are right," he murmured, "we do not dream great dreams."

But, indeed, those who did found themselves outsiders. People's vivacious interest in every day left little room for the building of great conceptions. Especially was this true of womankind. For a girl to erect a ladder to the sky was out of anybody's ken. And thus it was no wonder that within the dyer's house at Fontebranda consternation followed Catherine Benincasa's act of rebellion against her obvious destiny.

The day she cut her hair went down in the family annals of misfortune. Her mother, observing that the girl wore a veil tightly wound about her head, finally asked the reason for it. Catherine's conscious blush aroused suspicion. With one quick jerk Lapa snatched off the covering.

"What hast thou done?" A shriek of rage and horror followed the disclosure. "Lisa! Giacomo! Come quickly! Behold the ruin this wretched girl has made!"

Crying, cursing, beside herself, Lapa drew down upon the shrinking offender the indignation of the entire household. Even Benincasa agreed with his wife that cutting her hair would do Catherine no good. "It will grow again," they said, "and then thou wilt be betrothed with more certainty than ever."

Meanwhile the rebel was placed outside the family circle of approval. She was told that if she refused to be a good daughter she might try to be a good servant and wait upon them all. From early till late they kept her busy and required her to serve the meals in silence.

Serenely she accepted her fate. To herself she pretended that she was the handmaiden of the Lord. Instead of standing there ready to refill the wine pitcher or bring the lettuce and olive oil for the good dyer and his noisy wife, she made believe she had the everlasting bliss and honour to be in the household of the blessed Mary, of Jesus, and the Apostles. Therefore when a command was flung at her she turned upon the speaker such a look of radiant willingness that Benincasa glanced at his wife in despair. How was it possible to punish a child who seemed so pleased with her humble chores?

What she did find a penalty was to be obliged to share another's sleeping room and be forbidden ever to shut herself away. She had no privacy for prayers. One day her father, chancing to pass her half-open door, saw her there by the canopied bed upon her knees.

Hastily withdrawing, he said to himself: "Am I doing right? The dove of holiness rests upon my little daughter's head. Yet I punish her."

Catherine herself could not quite see the immediate outcome of her own decision. She was sure of her direction and certain the life of a nun was not for her. Yet she longed for the support and protection of the Church. If she could only be a Dominican! Often she wondered if she might disguise herself as a man and enter the Order.

One night, kept sleepless by her agonizing uncertainty, she had a waking dream of amazing vividness. She saw Saint Dominic himself holding out to her a robe of white and black. "Daughter," he said, "one day thou shalt wear this robe." She woke with a start. And suddenly she knew. She would join the Mantellate—the Third Order of San Domenico. Its vows of service and purity of living did not involve retirement from the world nor from earthly duties.

Joyously she went before the assembled family and told them her new resolution. "I shall stay here gladly as your servant—or if you make me leave you, I shall go. But I cannot—no, never can I accept marriage. I must be wedded only to my vow to serve God. Whatever happens I must become a Mantellata."

Her clasped hands, the burning conviction in her dark eyes, the quiet passion of her voice—these hushed all protest. Before her father's eyes rose a sudden vision. It was of Francis of Assisi pleading for his parent's blessing upon his resolution to serve God and humanity. That was over a hundred years ago. And since then his words, his life, the work of his followers had brought thousands upon thousands a new sense of the meaning of Christianity. It was not in the affectionate and reverent heart of Giacomo Benincasa to play the stubborn rôle of San Francesco's father. Then and there he made up his mind. In a firm voice he announced that Catherine was no longer to rest under the ban of disapproval.

"If she has chosen to give herself completely to the Lord of Heaven," he said, "how can we pretend to find this child a more worthy betrothal? Vex her no more. Let her follow the dictates of her heart without interference."

So far as Lapa was concerned, that was easier said than done. Her substitution of caresses and supervision in the place of censor affected Catherine as merely a different sort of oppression. She had now gathered herself up for a stern course of self-discipline and could make no use of her mother's homely wisdom nor of her cosiness. Having no other gifts to bestow, the poor woman watched her daughter in baffled anxiety.

"What art thou trying to do, my girl?" she would cry in terror. "Why dost thou hurt thy precious flesh with that chain about thy waist and that hair shirt on thy back? Thou goest without food and sleep! Why must thou pray so many hours before the Crucifix? My other children were good, but they never acted thus."

Catherine looked tenderly at the puzzled face. She could not explain her purpose, yet she knew her fate was not that of others. To her had been made known Christ's meaning when he said, "Blessed are they that do hunger and thirst after righteousness, for they shall be filled." But to be filled one must first be empty of all earthly desires. She meant to train her body to take no heed whether it was warm, fed and comfortable. She would train her mind to receive divine thoughts only. For this she had to have a will as strong as steel. She was as certain as she was of the sun in its heaven that if she were strong enough she might be used for some high purpose.

She took for her cell a tiny room at the back of the house which looked out on a narrow alleyway. Paved in brick, it contained nothing but a chest, a bench, a Crucifix on the wall. Over the small high window she kept the shutters closed. Here she pursued her education of the spirit. But at first it was continually interrupted. To her parents she was still merely a beloved child.

Often when Lapa found Catherine kneeling at night in prayer or lying sleepless on the wooden bench or tiled floor she would take her by force into her big bed. She tried to fling the soft comfort of her arms between her daughter and this vast and terrible Unknown. But, waking at dawn, the mother would find the place beside her empty.

Once, indeed, Lapa found Catherine lying on the floor, her robe streaked with blood. In fright and anguish the mother screamed so loud that the neighbours came running in. They found the poor woman tearing out her hair and digging her nails into her cheeks. "My daughter! She kills herself!" she shrieked. Learning the cause of her grief, the good folk went away shaking their heads and vowing Catherine mad.

To know herself the subject of curiosity was torture to the sensitive girl. But she felt that, too, was part of her education. What other people thought of her must become less than nothing. Her only solace was her own sense of progress. Every month of effort strengthened her will. At the end of a year she could subsist on a little bread and water. A few snatches of sleep were enough. Those messages which the brain sends to the body—I am cold, I am hungry—these she had learned to cut off completely. Lost in contemplation, she had no sense of her physical self.

Still Lapa kept hoping the stern resolve would pass. With relief she returned from her first inquiry concerning the Mantellate. It consisted of older women, all of them married or widowed and they refused to consider so young a person as Catherine for membership. Heartened by the news, Lapa took her wan daughter to the south in Val d'Orcia where there were healthful baths. A change might make her see reason.

All in vain. The girl, requesting to bathe alone, drew so near the boiling water as to run the risk of being burnt. The process exhausted her further. Hardly had she been brought home again when she took smallpox. Watching her day and night, Lapa feared this was the end. Most of her proffered services were refused. At last the anguished woman cried out, "Can I do nothing for thee, then?"

Immediately, with a smile of angelic sweetness, Catherine replied, "Go again and ask that I may enter the Mantellate. If they accept me I shall live."

This time Lapa was too much frightened not to do everything she could to persuade the Third Order of Saint Dominic to permit Catherine's joining them. A sister of Benincasa was a member and lent her influence, also, in favour of the girl. Yet there was no precedent for accepting so young a person. The membership insisted that a representative go and see if Catherine's beauty would be a drawback to her serious effort.

That individual, ushered into the sick-room by Lapa, saw only a thin, small girl upon her bed of pain, her pale face framed in short, tumbled hair. The visitor was quite satisfied. To an Italian woman of that period rich colouring, glorious tresses, full curves were the essentials of beauty. She questioned the candidate and was convinced of her earnestness.

"To become a Mantellata is the one wish of my heart, my path to Heaven!"

As Catherine said these words she lifted her glowing dark eyes, eloquent in the intensity of her desire. And then she smiled. A light seemed to flash from her white teeth and from her sparkling glance and the whole face became luminous with radiant vitality. To the seeing eye her beauty at such a moment was unearthly. But it was not that sort of eye which was estimating her attributes and it was not that sort of beauty which the Mantellata feared.

Soon after this visit, therefore, word was brought that Catherine had been made a member of the Tertiary Order. Lapa received the information with sinking heart. Well she knew that once robed in that black and white Dominican costume, her daughter was forever cut off from the sweet fulfilment of a girl's life. But when she went into the bedroom with

the news such a look of unutterable joy and gratitude flashed into the wan face that Lapa stood transfixed in wonder. It seemed years since she had seen
Catherine's face beam with happiness. It was beyond common understanding! But one thing was
immediately certain. The child would now recover.

For a long time after donning the white robe and
black mantle Catherine lived the life of a Carthusian monk. She never spoke if she could help it. She
never left her room except to go to San Domenico.
Father della Fonte was her confessor. He gave her
what instruction he could. But he could not follow
the stern path she was taking. Often enough he had
persuaded sinners they were doing wrong. But he
had never had anyone like her kneeling there before
him. Her standard was absolute perfection. She
blamed herself bitterly if she fell short by one
worldly thought, one impatient word, one moment
of self-indulgence. No one could guide her feet on
such heights. She had to climb alone.

One day, after many months of this régime, she
heard through her closed shutters the sound of
voices. She recognized one as belonging to her sister
and the other to one of her former friends, recently
a proud bride. It was the latter who said suddenly,
"What does Caterina do in that dark little room all
the time? So alone, so silent! She might as well be
dead!"

The listener laughed to hear. How could anyone
guess? True, she was a motionless pilgrim, but what
vast panoramas were unfolding before her! New
powers of soul, new knowledge came to her day by

day. To her marvelling spirit mysteries of existence
were made plain. Sharing a glorious communion,
she experienced ecstasy such as no earthly sensation
could afford. Often Father della Fonte found her
singing and received the joyous greeting of one
whose heart overflows with happiness.

Nevertheless, every portion of this growth was
attended by suffering. There was the terror of the
abyss into which her soul had to plunge to reach its
goal. And there was the unceasing call of youthful
happiness to meet. "Am I mistaken in giving it
up?" she would ask in profound self-question. In
such moments her isolation seemed like a wall of ice.

Even at San Domenico she met little sympathy.
The Brothers were annoyed at the tears she could
not restrain when taking communion. They found
embarrassing the trance-like state that seized her
at prayer and held her there after everyone else had
gone. One noonday the sexton and an assistant grew
weary of waiting to lock the door and be off to their
rabbit pie. Determinedly they picked up the prostrate form and laid it outside the church upon the
pavement. When the girl opened her eyes in the
broiling sun she was surrounded by gamins of
Fonte Branda. Howling with derision, they were
trying to rouse her by kicks and cuffs.

That little chapel at the far end of San Domenico
called the Cappella delle Volte was at once Catherine's refuge and the scene of her bitterest humiliation. Sometimes the bored priests refused her the
Sacrament. Once a very young Brother who thought
the Mantellata was faking her rapture, thrust a

great needle into her foot. She neither moved nor groaned. But when she rose to walk and found what had been done, the wound to her foot gave her no such pain as stabbed her heart.

Moreover, the very members of her own Order thought her penances unseemly. "Is she trying to set herself up as a model for us?" they asked one another indignantly.

The outcast had but one consolation—that suffering drew her nearer to the One who had suffered all. Furthermore, an enchanted avenue to new discovery lay before her. She persuaded one of the more friendly Mantellate to teach her to read. This meant, of course, that she had to read Latin. All the books of the Church and, indeed, most existing manuscripts were written in that universal language.

It was a difficult business. She would pore over the alphabet by the hour. Her family and everyone else who knew of her enterprise were dismayed afresh. For a woman to read Latin was proverbially a thing against nature. Undiscouraged, she persisted without cease. One day the closely written script at which she gazed suddenly had meaning. She looked further and still understood. Clapping her hands with almost incredulous delight, she cried aloud, "I can read! Blessed be God, I can read!"

With untiring enthusiasm she set to work. She read the Bible, breathed in the glory of the Psalms and caught fire from the eloquence of Saint Paul's Epistles. She learned to say Divine Office and read the Breviary. Then she pored over the lives of the Saints and now as she walked up the hill to hear

Mass she felt that Santa Lucia and Santa Agnesia were beside her. If the small boys hooted at her, she paid no heed.

Catherine Benincasa had now passed her eighteenth year. In this period of intensive work she felt that she had lived many lives. For she had attained self-knowledge. This meant that she had felt the crushing evil of the world and had taken it on her conscience. But it also meant an ever-present sense of the triumphant Love which pulsed unceasing like the heart beat of the Earth.

One evening, however, that marvellous sureness failed her. The old torment of long ago rose within her stronger than ever. As she knelt on the brick pavement of her cell, she felt that all the spirits of hell were beating around her.

Through her closed shutters came the gleeful din of bells, shouts of merrymakers, riotous songs, the notes of horns. Every breeze carried the smell of sizzling sausages and the fruity fragrance of the good red wine of Chianti. For it was Carnival time. Lustily the folk of Fontebranda were giving themselves to the gross hilarity of the hour. That morning Catherine had seen the booths set up, the taverns crowded. She had caught a glimpse of rollicking youths, sauntering near Camporeggi with their arms about laughing girls.

"Lord God, quicken Thou my faith!"

Thus Catherine prayed, alone in the midst of revel. Every quivering nerve told her that outside her narrow cell personal happiness was calling. That intense capacity for vision which she had developed now betrayed her. With a clarity that made her senses reel she pictured herself as a maiden such as she had seen that morning. She felt the warmth of a protecting arm about her, the sweetness of tender words breathed within her ear.

To love and be loved—ah, dear and tempting destiny! What else on earth was certain? For one awful instant it seemed to the girl that all her great quest was a thing of her imagination only. If Christ and the Spiritual World were not true, then to what end sacrifice and discipline? For the Truth one could give all. But suppose she were deceived? What if the whole vast fabric of that other world were but a radiant bubble filled with the breath of human longing?

"Lord God, quicken Thou my faith!"

Not once in all these years had she met this doubt. Her heart stopped with the terror of it. She pressed her forehead wet with anguish upon the tiles before the Crucifix. It was an instant far worse than death.

Suddenly the hideous pressure lifted. Warmth and radiance stole over her. Floating free from those lacerating weights, her soul rose before a Presence. It was more absolute than the flame of the little lamp above her head. Her inner ear caught a message clear as a trumpet note blown across frosty distances. And now she knew! This was Reality and none other. Deeper and deeper into her consciousness sank the bliss of this acceptance. Never before had she felt so merged in the Oneness of Divinity. Here within her was Life and she was part of it forever.

When she returned to a sense of where she was the streets outside were silent. Softly through the deep peace she heard the bell calling the Brothers to Matin service. The Carnival was over.

Three days after this Catherine, deep in meditation, felt something flash through her. It was the meaning of that revelation that had been the seal upon her long period of trial. Now she must go forth into the world again. Trembling, she pushed the idea from her. She was not yet strong enough. Retirement, contemplation were so safe, so sweet. But gradually she was forced to recognize that this, too, was the self demanding its own way. Had she not been given knowledge? She must use it for others. Resolutely she arose. Opening her door, she walked straight across the terrace into the family kitchen.

To enter the Benincasa circle once more was for Catherine exactly like coming into a noisy square glaring with noonday sun after years of silence and darkness. It was horrible. The clack of tongues over nothing, the smell of greasy food, the jostling of personalities. The house was more crowded than ever with the families of Catherine's married brothers and of her step-brother who had all come to live there. It was only the children playing and laughing on the staircase who eased the shock of that inauguration.

Soon, however, Catherine gained a friend in Lisa, the wife of her half-brother. Lisa was of the Colombini family. Her cousin was Giovanni Colombini who had given up wealth and position to found an Order of Poverty. Despite a fanaticism which had been the talk of Siena, his sincerity had converted many a rich young man to follow him. Perhaps the sympathy with which Lisa had followed the transformation in her worldly relative gave her understanding of Catherine. At any rate, unlike the rest of the household, she thought the girl's strangeness beautiful, her occasional words full of inspired wisdom.

Lovingly she helped Catherine through that difficult period of adjustment. The hermit of three years at once took up her share of work in this huge beehive. But, though her hands were skilled, she was not always accountable. If she followed a thought into the realm where she had dwelt so long she would lose all sense of what she was doing. The spoon would drop from her hand. The bread would burn or the kettle spill. And then Monna Lapa's exasperation would explode. To rescue her from these mishaps Lisa took to following the girl about like a shadow.

There was, however, no saving Catherine from the consequences of her own nature. In his joy over the return of his daughter Giacomo Benincasa told her she could give what she wished to the poor. All his life he had been charitable. But he was not prepared for the lavish literalness with which she took him at his word. She would like to give everything away. Barrels of flour and quantities of clothes disappeared before that unearthly passion of generosity could be tempered. Lisa tried to explain. "Giovanni Colombini likewise wished to give away the money he had made. He invited the poor to his house, fed them and dressed them in his newest garments. His wife was not so much in love with poverty as he, but she saw that he could not do otherwise. It is like that with Catherine."

The argument did not reconcile Lapa. She was scandalized one day to see her daughter returning home from Camporeggi in her white robe only. The black mantle was gone. For any woman to appear on the street without some sort of cloak marked her as an outcast from society. "What hast thou done with thy *mantello*?" demanded the mother, aghast.

"I gave it to a half-naked beggar," replied the girl calmly. Then to Lapa's vociferous protest she made an answer that has been quoted throughout all the centuries. "Better to be without a cloak than without charity."

Those compassionate hands could hardly find activity enough. Catherine began at once to enter into the service which the members of the Mantellate regularly undertook for the sick. Both to the great hospital near the Duomo and to the Mercy Hospital near her house, she went constantly. Because she had conquered the need of sleep she was particularly valuable in caring for night cases. Messer Matteo Cenni, the director of the Misericordia, observed her skill and devotion with much admiration and soon became her friend.

At the hospital of Santa Maria della Scala in the vast and vaulted room where the sick beds lay close together Catherine's perspective expanded hour by hour. Not only did she learn much of other people's sufferings. But in that place where every type of being came for one reason or another, she began to find out what was going on in the world. It was there she first heard men speak with passionate protest against the location of the Papal See at Avignon. Most people she knew, even the Dominican Brothers, felt only a philosophic regret due to sixty years' endurance of the Pope's exile.

Naturally enough the discussions at the hospital centred on religious matters. For it was not knowledge of medicine that drew men to this service for their fellows. It was an expression of the love of God. A religious confraternity ran the hospital and all the nurses were, like Catherine, connected in some way with the Church.

One day the Brothers and Sisters greeted Catherine's entrance with joyous excitement. News was always brought to the hospital and this time it seemed good beyond belief.

"The Pope is leaving Avignon!" they cried, pressing about her in the dim corridor. "He will restore the Holy See in Rome. Already he has set sail and will land at Corneto. We have learned that the blessed Giovanni Colombini has gone to get his blessing upon his Order of Poverty."

Every Italian, whether Guelf or Ghibelline, rejoiced in this tremendous event. It meant that at last French dominance of the Papacy was at an end. This had begun in 1305 when a French cardinal had been elected head of the Church. Influenced by the French king, Philip the Fair, he had never stepped foot out of France. His successor, also a Frenchman, established a permanent and magnificent residence in Avignon and there followed seven French Popes in all of whom national feeling dictated the policy of remaining in Provence. Italians believed—and with reason—that only from Rome, the traditional centre of leadership, could the Papacy maintain over Christendom a sway which defied national barriers. What they did not fully admit was the state of anarchy in Rome, evinced by the curious career of Cola di Rienzi, which offered insufficient peace and protection to the Popes.

Religious men declared that the faults and abuses, the worldliness and contention within the Church were due to this unnatural exile of its head. Poets like Dante and Petrarch had thundered against the Pope's foreign residence and declared that all hope of peace and reformation hung upon his return to Rome. It was therefore with exultant hearts that the entire country followed Urban Fifth's brave attempt to leave the luxurious and corrupt city of Avignon.

This momentous proceeding did much to draw Catherine Benincasa's heart into the affairs of her time. Moreover, in this same year of 1367 her interest in local matters was suddenly aroused. For her own brother Bartolommeo was elected one of the Twelve Governors of Siena.

Lapa was in high feather over this honour. "Do you know," she would cry, "that my son is now called 'Magnificent Lord'?" And when she went to market on the Campo she carried herself with the pride of knowing she now belonged to the ruling class of the Republic.

Thus in a brief twelve months after leaving her cell Catherine's days became crowded with new experience, new contacts, new friends. Among the latter who were to remain close to her for the rest of her days were two members of the Mantellate— Francesca Gori, called Cecca for short, and Alessa Saracini, of an old and noble family. These women, together with Lisa who had also joined the Tertiaries, clung to her as to their natural leader.

From Camporeggi came another friend to join the nucleus of that circle which was to widen first throughout Siena and then throughout all Italy. Tommaso della Fonte brought to the house in Fonte Branda another Dominican, Father Bartolommeo. The latter had been helping della Fonte set down in writing some of the marvellous conversations he had had with Catherine. Yet, impressed as Fra Bartolommeo was with the extraordinary personality of this young woman, he cherished a certain scepticism concerning her vaunted gifts.

Already a legend was growing up about her amongst the people. Beggars told tales of her miraculously filling pitchers of wine from an empty barrel. Friends reported that her unlighted little room often became filled with unearthly illumination. Others declared that so swiftly did Catherine's loaves rise for the baking that the Virgin Mary's hand had helped her. Everyone agreed that the girl had second sight and could read minds.

That these latter powers were fact Father Bartolommeo one day discovered for himself. Resolving to test the girl, he asked her what he had been doing at nine o'clock the previous evening. Since he had been absolutely alone, he knew that nobody could have told her.

"You were writing," said Catherine promptly.

"Writing what?" he asked in astonishment. When she told him the exact matter on which he had been engaged, he felt his heart pervaded by a feeling of deep reverence. What powers of soul this child of God had developed in those years of isolation!

But those years were over. Catherine Benincasa was beginning to take that place which was to make her one of the great figures of all time. And the strange and stormy years of 1368 and 1369 were important milestones in her glorious destiny.

Chapter Three

TWELVE deep strokes, muffled yet reso-
nant, floated from the great tower of the
Palazzo della Signoria. They marked
high noon on this March day of the year
1368. Already the market people had closed their
stalls. Usually, indeed, at this hour when all the
town was filled with succulent odours from cook-
pots the square was almost empty. But today a crowd
hung about the palace.

Students in short cloaks and saucy caps irrever-
ently jostled the many gentlemen and nobles gathered near the great central doorway. Gossip had it
that these sessions of the Twelve Governors had
grown stormy. And lately all who feared plots or
loved excitement had come to pick up news.

One handsome fellow in a plumed hat turned impatiently to the older man beside him. "My father," said he, "albeit the Twelve will shortly come forth, they will tell us nothing. Let me go in and have a word with some one."

"Go, Stefano," said his father in a low voice, "it may mean much to the house of Maconi to discover which way the wind blows."

Stefano Maconi had grown to manhood since that evening he had dined after the hunt with his friend Francesco. Now, tall and of gallant bearing, he had become his father's aid in the contests which forever engaged the noble houses of Siena. Nobody was quicker with the sword than he. Even as he turned away his fingers on the jewelled hilt itched to use it against those treacherous, ambitious Salimbeni who, so rumour had it, plotted to seize the ruling power.

For more than seventy years the government of the Republic had been in the hands of men engaged in trades, crafts and professions. The nobles, eligible only to an advisory body, fumed at their lack of responsibility. And no family resented its powerlessness so much as the Salimbeni. Bankers for more than a century, they held, despite some sensational financial failures, the distinction of being the richest and most potent house in the city. For this they were cordially detested by their peers.

Stefano Maconi strode into the hall and started up the wide, dark stairway. Already clerks, notaries and pages were coming down. At the top of the steps, the newcomer pushed past two men-at-arms and entered the great Room of the Crossbows.

There, brilliant in the March sunshine, the superb equestrian mural by Simone Martine dominated the shifting, buzzing crowd.

Stefano's eyes danced to observe immediately one man he knew. Moving importantly from one group to another, this officious fellow kept an unmistakably rustic air which his notary costume failed to disguise. It was Cristofano di Gano Guidini, recently established in Siena as notary to the Captain of the People. Stefano's acquaintance with him dated back to the time when several of his boyhood friends had been tutored by the good man when the latter was in the city as a student.

Advancing toward the bustling figure, the young man called out, "Greetings, Messer di Gano!" Then, before the latter could do more than beam upon him, he added in an undertone, "What news today from the Hall of the Nine?"

This name still clung to the council chamber. Yet the Nine who had governed so long and so well had been deposed long ago and now twelve men constituted the Signoria or body of rulers. A powerful position was theirs. They chose the chief executive or Podestà; they appointed the collectors and disbursers of the taxes; they passed laws, executed judgment on the enemies of the Republic and decided on offensive and defensive wars.

Messer di Gano impressively laid a finger beside his long nose. "Something is afoot," said he cautiously. "But, though I was called in to present a notation half an hour since, I cannot rightly tell what argument divides the council."

At that moment the door into the high vaulted chamber was swung open. Two by two the rulers of the Republic in their sober robes pushed forward. If they showed a certain haste to be gone it was small wonder. They had been on duty since seven in the morning. Indeed, each one had to be at his place before the great bell ceased to ring or else be penalized by fine. To revive his lagging attention a governor had but to look about the walls. There the explicit brush of Ambrogio Lorenzetti had painted vast allegories of Good Government—Justice enthroned amid all the virtues, peace and prosperity everywhere. Dimly one can still see those knights and ladies ride smiling through the town and happy peasants bring their produce through hospitable gates.

Deferentially the crowd fell back to let the Twelve pass. But to young Maconi's amused delight his friend the notary touched one of them upon the arm and said obsequiously, "Magnificent Lord, is it possible to have a word with you?"

Readily enough the man stepped aside. Above Cristofano's head to the handsome youth behind him his dark eyes travelled swiftly and in them was recognition. Often had this man watched the young Maconi gallop through the streets and had long since identified him as the son of that Messer Currado for whom so many rolls of cloth had been dyed at the shop in Fonte Branda. Now, however, by the turn of Fate's wheel the dyer's son was a member of the ruling class and had a hand in events likely to affect the young nobleman's fortune.

Hesitatingly the notary was saying, "Messer Bartolommeo Benincasa, is it made known yet what affair stirs the council chamber?"

Deliberately Bartolommeo exerted his right to lordliness. "Truly, Messer di Gano, nothing may be revealed of our transactions—save, perhaps, that a deputation may be sent to the Pope at Rome. Good day to you!" With a formal bow, Benincasa moved toward the staircase.

Shrugging his discomfited shoulders, the notary turned to Stefano. "Trouble may be brewing and if you long for a fight do not despair. But I doubt if discord among the Twelve yet means danger to the city's peace."

Slowly the two joined the throng descending the broad stairs. Maconi wished impatiently that things would come to the boiling point. It would be glorious to take part in a real battle. He'd like to show these ruling tradesmen a thing or two. Suddenly aware of the question his companion had just put to him, he roused himself to answer.

"Messer Ranieri di Landoccio dei Pagliaresi?" he echoed gropingly. "*Per Dio*, I have not seen him for five years! He returns here sometimes from his studies in Perugia and Francesco Malavolti sees him, but not I. Soon I believe he will finish and come back. A learned youth, indeed!"

Joining his father in the Campo, Stefano took leave of his companion and turned homewards. As he did so he noticed again the man whom the notary had addressed in the palace. Benincasa had halted in his progress across the piazza and was greeting a woman walking swiftly toward him. Observing that the small figure wore the costume of a Mantellata, Stefano thought of something his friend Francesco had once said. "The Third Order represents the only free women of Italy," Malavolti had declared. "They come and go exactly as they please and when I marry I shall never let my wife become a Tertiary."

Something of the same resentment tinged the tone in which Bartolommeo was addressing his sister. "Caterina, hast thou been again to the Lazar house to nurse that old leper Tecca?"

For answer she gave him a look. It was the very essence of that objectionable freedom of spirit. Calm, assured, it made no challenge to approval or disapproval. With a sunny smile the girl merely nodded in reply to her brother's question.

"Thou takest that long walk beyond the Porta Nuova. Thou bringest her food and carest for her filthy, leprous body and thy reward is abuse. She talks scandal of thee and still thou goest to her!"

At this the girl winced. It was true enough. This very morning old Tecca had burst out, "Ho, Queen of Fonte Branda! Thou art late. Thou canst not attend a poor sick woman. No, the Queen must go to the church of the Brothers! All morning she must spend with the Brothers!"

Such implied slander from those ungrateful lips had been heard by all the other workers at the pest-house and duly carried back to Lapa and her sons. That they protested Catherine's daily visit in vain aroused Bartolommeo's anger. "Thou wilt end by catching the disease and infecting us all!" he raged.

As they walked swiftly onward in silence, Catherine stole a look at her hands. Coming from the fetid place, she had seen upon them a suspicious redness. But now they were smooth and white again. Serenely she turned to her brother and inquired what had happened that morning in the Hall of the Nine. When he told her of the deputation to the Pope her face glowed with joy.

"The Vicar of Christ ploughs the field of God!" she exclaimed. "Messer Matteo of the Misericordia says the Holy Father restores in Rome the ruin at Saint John Lateran, at Saint Peter's and Saint Paul's. His entry into the city was a triumph of Righteousness and he has brought the rose of peace to blossom there. Let us pray it fades not!"

At almost every step toward Fonte Branda that noonday Catherine received some word of greeting. Women, shop-keepers, children, beggars—all would call out a blessing as she passed. For that small figure in black mantle and white robe, taking its fleet way of service, had become one of the most familiar in the city.

Yet it was not many weeks after this that Catherine was to taste the bitterness lurking in the cup of fame. At the far eastern end of the city stood the church of the Franciscans. This Order, founded by a man who lived without possessions that he might devote his entire heart to God, had spread all over Italy and had founded convents and churches everywhere. As its property increased, however, a spirit of pride and even luxury had invaded certain of its members. Such a man was Father Lazzarino. An intellectual and a scholar, he had come to Siena from Pisa some years ago to preach at San Francesco and lecture on philosophy at the University. His influence in cultured circles was immense.

One day in his lecture this man held up as an example of hypocrisy and pretentiousness a maid named Catherine Benincasa. An ignorant creature claiming to be a holy servant of God! Bitterly he derided the ecstasies she experienced, the miracles she was supposed to have achieved. Upon the whole Dominican Order he heaped scorn for tolerating her deceptions. From that time forward, the learned man never spoke from the platform without vilifying the virgin of Fonte Branda. To do so had become an obsession with him.

His students, who were sons of small nobles, rich merchants, bankers and lawyers, brought back word of these attacks. Their elders in cynical amusement discussed the rivalry between the two Orders. Many were ready to wager that Fra Bartolommeo of San Domenico, who also lectured at the University, would soon be laughed out of his post. Indeed, that individual was constantly interrupted in his discourse by rude students demanding, "Tell us of Catherine Benincasa and how she got the ear of God!"

With gentle dignity Father Bartolommeo would reply, "Her goodness is very great. She has freed her spirit from all thought of self. She sees deeply into human hearts. Such is her only claim to holiness."

Late in the spring a morning came when the University buzzed with excitement. Students told one another the news on the stairs and corridors. Father Lazzarino had resigned. Madder than that —he who had the finest collection of illuminated books in Siena was giving them away to any person who would come and take them. What did it mean? Did he repent his rage against the maid of Fonte Branda?

It was long before the true story was known. But all who heard it found laughter dying on their lips. For what had happened was, indeed, strange. One afternoon Father Lazzarino had asked his enemy Fra Bartolommeo to take him to Catherine's house. She received him quietly and serenely parried his ironic request for spiritual guidance. When he left, quite baffled, she knelt to ask his blessing and to his dry request that she pray for him she returned a fervent promise that she would.

Late that night the Franciscan started to prepare his next day's lecture. But he could not fix his mind upon the work. He found himself beset with so profound a melancholy that the tears ran down his cheeks. On the morrow he had to give up his classes and remain in his room.

In despair he searched his mind for the cause of this unknown grief. At once a picture sprang before him. It showed a tiny, barren room and in it a small figure garbed in black and white. He felt upon his face two grave, questioning eyes. There followed another image of this same figure bending over an old leper in the pest-house and receiving her dying confession of penitence and gratitude. Suddenly Lazzarino turned his head and looked about his luxurious apartment as if for the first time. Gorgeous hangings and rugs, a soft couch, a fire, costly books—did these belong to a follower of the Little Brother of the Poor? Like snapping cords burst the pride about the Franciscan's heart. He rushed back to Fonte Branda.

In that same little room he knelt at the feet of the girl he had condemned. Sobbing out his repentance, he cried out, "Tell me, how may I atone for my life of ease?"

She had received him without surprise. Now a look of joyful tenderness was bent upon his face. For hours they talked—the middle-aged savant, the girl of twenty-one. When he went away it was with a heart so light that he seemed to be floating through space and before a week was up he had taken himself to an hermitage in Pisa.

This dramatic instance of Catherine's growing power—discussed so eagerly in cultured circles— brought to a close the first half of the year. July was somnolent with the brewing of political storms. Everyone knew now what the Maconi had tried to find out that March morning. The Salimbeni family had hatched a definite plot to overthrow the government and had carried half of the twelve governors with them. The other six had joined with the rest of the nobles in opposition to the Salimbeni.

Excitement and foreboding pervaded every

house. One day in August this general anxiety was intensified by the arrival of a courier with news which caused the head of each family to call a hasty conference. In the Malavolti palace, however, this gathering preserved a semblance of sociability. The men were seated at a long table in the loggia at the top of the house and before them wine and spiced cakes were set out. Yet these were scarcely touched. The group was too much absorbed in discussing the impending event. This was the reappearance of Charles Fourth. Already he had crossed the mountains into Italy on his way to be crowned by the Pope at Rome.

"What I have learned," said the senior Malavolti impressively, "is that these cursed Salimbeni will attempt to win the Emperor to their side. Then, supported by Carlo's forces, they will overthrow the government, elect whom they will and hold the power of the Republic."

"True, but they may not win," said his eldest son. "The party of opposition, headed by the Tolomei, intends sending ambassadors also to the Emperor. And with all the other nobles joining forces the Salimbeni may be defeated. The swords of the Malavolti should make that defeat a certainty."

Francesco Malavolti, the same debonair young man who had praised Folgore's poem on the hunt, had taken little part in the argument. Leaning on the parapet, he stood looking in the direction of a certain house. Somewhere across the towered city a girl was sending him her winged thoughts. For recently Francesco's parents had settled the question of his marriage. And he wondered, half fearfully, what it would mean to him to have a wife.

At his brother's last words, however, he turned back to the table. Somewhat satirically he eyed the group. Then he drawled: "Remember, all of you, that you can hardly join this fray. You who hate the Tolomei to the death cannot side with them— even though you may hate the Salimbeni more. Let these noble houses fall upon each other is my counsel. The Salimbeni have no one with them but 'the Little People.' Even if the Emperor supports them they cannot hold power long. Every Guelf family in Siena will be out to fight imperial interference."

In the silence that followed this speech a look of admiration dawned in the eyes fixed upon Francesco. Finally his father said: "For all thy youth, my son, thou hast wisdom. Let us wait then and see. Doubtless we can crush the party of the Salimbeni later without alliance with enemy houses. More than one battle is like to follow on this plot."

After the clan had agreed to this, one of the older men said in a tone of commiseration, "I fear, Francesco, with so many friends under arms, thou art fated to have a quiet nuptial celebration."

At the young man's rueful expression the others laughed and, lifting their glasses of red Orvieto wine, cried out, "Viva! Health to the Bride and Bridegroom!"

Francesco bowed. Then, goblet in hand, he added

vehemently, "And down with the plotting members of the Twelve!"

One of the governors thus condemned to destruction lived just down the hill from the Malavolti palace on the slope over Fonte Branda. Yes, Bartolommeo Benincasa had thrown in his lot with the Salimbeni. Each day he returned from the Signoria worn with the friction of these clashing elements. He pretended to no certainty of results.

That fact would certainly have terrorized his household had it not been for a great grief which hung over it. Toward the middle of August the good Giacomo, the head and father of the family, fell seriously ill. As Lapa and her daughters-in-law worked in a frantic effort to save him, they looked in amazement at Catherine. Motionless and calm she sat beside the couch. Often the tears ran down her cheeks. Yet her look of uplifted joy was never displaced. From the first she seemed to foresee the end, and when her father died she was ready to comfort the others.

"Death is the Deliverer," she said to them tenderly. "It is God's grace to man. Let us not grieve —except over our weak grief."

Lisa, watching the girl's ecstatic face during the Dead Mass chanted for Giacomo at San Domenico, believed she was following that departed spirit into the region of the dead. "Such a one makes a bridge from Heaven to earth," she thought with reverence.

Resignedly the three Benincasa brothers took up the management of the dyeing business. Bartolommeo, however, was deeply involved in the coming civic struggle. The Emperor was approaching from the north of Italy now and his daughter with a large escort preceded him into the city.

Still in doubt as to which party the Emperor would favour, the citizens all turned out to welcome this emissary. On a milk-white horse, in a robe of gold, topped by a blue mantle lined with fur, the German Princess smiled graciously upon the cheering crowds. The city magistrates escorted her to the inn they had selected for her entertainment. Dismounting at the Albergo del Gallo, she received impartially deputations from both the Salimbeni and their rivals.

It was the last moment of peace the city was to know for many moons. Battles small and large followed one upon another. At first, with the Emperor supporting them, the Salimbeni triumphed. It was they who after a fierce fight marched with olive branches in their hands and wreaths upon their heads to welcome the Emperor at the Porta Camoillia.

"As he entered," wrote a chronicler of the day, "there was no other sound but 'Viva, Viva' and the people carried him the keys of the gates and presented him with the treasure chest and said to him 'Help yourself'! And he dismounted at the Salimbeni house and had with him 1,000 horsemen and 500 men-at-arms and all were lodged and sheltered in houses of gentlemen."

With all the defeated nobles banished from the city, the Salimbeni were rewarded both by the Emperor and by the government they themselves had

created. The former knighted the family. The latter granted them castles and the title "Of the
People" which made them eligible to rule—a truly
Republican honour. In triumph the Salimbeni escorted the royal party to Mass at the Cathedral.
Trumpeters in long scarlet stockings led the way.
Pages held over the heads of Emperor and Empress
magnificent canopies made at the command of the
commune.

To view that gorgeous pageant Lapa and her
daughters-in-law dragged Catherine to the great
square. Pressed by the crowd close against the marble steps of the Duomo, the four women saw Bartolommeo Benincasa, one of the handsomely dressed
magistrates, marching with the victors. Lapa cried
out in triumph and hurried the others after the
procession into the cathedral. There in the light of
thousands of candles, in the rich aroma of incense,
in the majestic vibrations of a mighty cantata, the
ceremony set the seal on temporal glory.

Catherine did not join the others at the celebration. Instead, she slipped across the square to that
vast Gothic building, Santa Maria della Scala,
where the cost of this victory was being reckoned
up. Already the place was full of wounded and
dying. And in the months that followed the girl
laboured incessantly to bind up wounds from spear
and dagger. Her hands were tender, but her soul
seethed with rebellion against the insane waste of
these futile struggles carried on by the enemies of
the Salimbeni. Outside the city walls the banished
nobles laid waste the countryside. Within, their con-

federates fought without cease the troops which the Emperor left behind him under his lieutenant, Malatesta.

At last the government set up by the Salimbeni fell. Then everyone who had been a party to it was in danger. One evening at sunset Catherine returned home from La Scala to find the entire family gathered in the kitchen amid an indescribable hubbub. Between Lapa's shrieks and the wailing of the children the girl managed to discover the cause of the uproar. In the midst of the group stood a neighbour. He had just rushed in to say that armed men were hunting the town for allies of the Salimbeni.

Grasping Bartolommeo and his brother by the arm, this man was shouting: "You must fly at once! To the church of San Antonio! All are taking refuge there!"

"No, not there!"

Startled by the ringing words, everyone in the room turned toward the small, erect figure in the doorway. During these weeks of constant service Catherine had been little with her family. Often she spent the night at La Scala, kneeling between vigils in the small vaulted chapel beneath the hospital rooms. Now it was as if she had reappeared from some spot far distant from the wild fury of the city.

In the silence following her words, she spoke again with prophetic authority. "All who hide in San Antonio are lost. Come with me and fear not!"

The neighbour made a move to protest. Not so the others. Never had they trusted Catherine in vain. Her brothers hastened to her side and, half covering them with her mantle, she led them up the steep street. For an instant when they reached the top they thought their end had come. Two men with daggers ready sprang out upon them. But Catherine did not check her step. One look from her and the assailants fell back helplessly. Mystified they let her pass with her muffled companions. Straight to the Hospital of Mercy she led them and placed them under the protection of the rector, Messer Matteo. Hardly had she returned home when the grim news came that all the refugees at San Antonio had been set upon and slain.

Scarcely had the year 1369 begun when the Salimbeni made one last effort to regain control of the city. At their behest the Emperor on his way back from Rome flung his three thousand men into the fray. The battle raged in every street and all the bells clanged warnings of disaster.

In one corner of the Campo, which was a mass of struggling men in armour, two young warriors were smiting their enemies side by side. So hot was the fight that they had had no time to exchange a word. Yet Francesco Malavolti rejoiced that beside him Stefano Maconi was there with his good sword. For hours without rest they laid about them. Once a spear caught Stefano in the shoulder. But when his friend had stuffed a scarf under his breastplate he fought on lustily as ever.

At last with the retreat of the imperial forces to a nearby street there came a lull in the combat.

Seizing this moment, Francesco asked his companion how he had chanced to join in the defence.

"*Per Dio!*" shouted young Maconi, "all the Guelfs are out today. Carlo shall gain no hold in our Republic while we live to defend it. The Salimbeni are lost. Look there!"

He pointed to a horseman galloping towards the Captain of the People, an olive branch before him. It was one of the Salimbeni. Realizing he had come to sue for peace, the two young men hurried forward to hear the captain's answer.

"Go back!" they heard the captain shout. "Tell Carlo his men lie in heaps by the Fonte Gaia. Tell him his own nephew has been slain. There will be no peace till we have won the day!"

By sunset the Guelf nobles and their party had proved completely victorious. When the Emperor's men retreated to his stronghold, the Salimbeni palace, a herald was sent up and down to forbid any citizen to take them food or succour. Picking their way between the dead, Stefano and Francesco mounted their horses and left the Campo. As they rode along cheers from the windows above the street testified to the general rejoicing in the Emperor's defeat.

Already Francesco's lively spirits had turned back to the current of every day. He leaned toward his companion saying, "You have not seen my bride, Stefano. Thanks to this cursed embroglio my wedding was almost a secret affair. Even Neri di Landoccio did not come from Perugia to attend it.

But truly she is a girl of great beauty. Just fifteen and with the sweetness of an angel!"

Shyly Stefano felicitated his friend. Then he said with an embarrassed grin, "Negotiations for my marriage have been broken off. It would seem I live only to fight. But today I rejoice in that. We have made Carlo know his mistake in supporting the Salimbeni." Saluting Malavolti in farewell, he turned into the Maconi courtyard.

Stefano's last words were prophetic. According to the chronicler, "the emperor was frightened and he wept and embraced and kissed all who came to him and said he was betrayed." The moment the Sienese offered him money to leave the city he took it and departed thankfully. Yet despite their defeat, the party of the Salimbeni kept the city in such turmoil that finally ambassadors had to be sent to Florence requesting that Republic to settle the dispute. Their basis of agreement between people and nobles was accepted and amid glad bells and wild rejoicing peace was made at last.

No one was more grateful for peace than Catherine Benincasa. She made instant use of her resulting leisure to gratify a longing felt for months. It was to understand why this strife into which she had been thrust had befallen her city. She had a sure source of information in her friend, Alessa Saracini. Belonging as she did to a proud and ancient family, that young woman had grown up with an intimate knowledge of local intrigue.

Alessa asked nothing better than to put at Catherine's disposal her unusual education and experience.

As an independent widow, the young noblewoman
had the entrée of the most exclusive social group.
But since she was childless, her desire to be of some
use in the world had impelled her to join the
Mantellate. And when she met Catherine Benincasa all other contacts seemed to her dull and
empty. She and her mother took a house near the
Benincasas and now she persuaded the girl to spend
with her a great part of that year.

Alessa's history lessons gave Catherine the scope
and perspective for judging the affairs, not only of
Siena, but of Italy. Her inner life of contemplative
vision, however, had long since passed the bounds of
human guidance. Only her confessor, Father della
Fonte, was even dimly aware of those ever-
expanding spiritual horizons. What her friends did
observe was the effect of this unearthly insight upon
all the human beings she encountered. Unhappy
married couples, grieving widows, puzzled mothers,
sufferers of all kinds sought out her counsel and her
consolation. And never in vain.

Amongst them all no one impressed Alessa more
than a young monk who presented himself one day.
The distinction of his features and his glowing eyes
were in vivid contrast to his brown habit and bare
feet. Briefly he told Catherine of his work at the
monastery—the gardening, the preparation of
meals, the thousand and one small services exacted
during each interminable day.

Clasping his thin, work-worn hands, he cried
out, "Mother, I find too little time for meditation

and for prayer. It was for these I wished to be a monk."

In silence Catherine's eyes rested upon him with maternal tenderness. She thought of her own childish struggle to be alone in her bustling household. Yet no one knew better than she that service for others was the true Christian ideal. Gently she said in her musical voice, "You must pray the prayer of action which is the fragrant flowering of the soul. I, too, am living that prayer now." Then as a look of consolation stole over the monk's yearning face, she added exultantly, "A good man *is* a prayer."

It was difficult, however, for Catherine to solace those who came tormented by the evil they saw within the Church. Sin, selfishness and greed among those whose vows meant dedication to God acted like poison upon unbalanced minds. In one monastery the monks rebelled against the duties and penances which the heads of the Order did not themselves obey. In another, the Brothers rose up and slew their Superior. It was small wonder that Catherine's loving service to all who came her way seemed like a light in darkness. Yet it was with surprise that her intimates discovered one day how deep a mark she had already made upon the hearts of her townsfolk.

One August Sunday in 1370 Fra Bartolommeo was preaching at San Domenico. His flock, listless from the heat and wearied from the recent excitement of the public games and jousting matches, were apathetically listening. Suddenly an electric shock ran through the audience. A whisper passed from one to another. Faces blanched. Members of the Tertiary Order murmured together in consternation. As the commotion increased, the preacher caught the words, "Catherine Benincasa is dead."

Bringing his sermon to an abrupt close, Fra Bartolommeo hurried into the sacristy. There he found a lay brother in an anguish of grief over the news. Both men rushed to the Benincasa house. They discovered a crowd outside. The stairway was a milling mass of people. Pushing their way into Catherine's room, they found her lying lifeless on her couch. Lapa, Father della Fonte, Lisa and Alessa were gathered there—despair on every face. Each of these people had many times seen Catherine in a trance, but this state was absolutely different. There was no breath in that limp body.

With anguished sobs the lay brother flung himself upon the tiles before the couch. As he did so a gush of blood spouted from his lungs. Alessa, fearful for his life, tried to draw him away. But the man seized Catherine's hand and pressed it to his lips. Immediately the hæmorrhage ceased. At the same instant the inanimate form stirred. Catherine's eyelids lifted and her fathomless regard turned upon her friends. In passionate thanksgiving they sank to their knees or pressed around her. Their joyful exclamations, carried outside, echoed like a pæan on the stairs and in the street.

But the girl herself did not share the general elation. A shudder accompanied her return to consciousness. Turning her face to the wall, she broke into bitter sobs and could not be comforted for many days. No one understood the anguish she experienced in that abrupt return from her far journey. All she could say was, "I saw the hidden things of God and now I am thrust back into the prison of the body."

That prison was made more grim by grievous news. The head of Christendom, Urban Fifth, had proved unequal to his bravely undertaken task. Urged by his cardinals, the majority of whom were French, afflicted by ill-health, plagued by the disorders at Rome, he found irresistible his longing for the fair lands of Provence. Toward the end of that summer the Pope turned his face toward Avignon. In vain all Italy protested. A Roman embassy pleaded with Urban to remain. Petrarch sped an eloquent message to combat his resolution. Deputies were sent from many cities to beg him not to leave Rome.

One day toward the middle of September, Father Bartolommeo and Fra Tommaso brought the ultimate word to Catherine and Alessa. "The Father has abandoned his children," they said mournfully. "On September fifth he sailed from Corneto. Already he is once more in that seat of all corruption on the borderland of France."

Catherine bowed her stricken head. In these months of tutelage Alessa had made it clearer to her than ever why the peace and unity of Italy depended on the presence of the Pope at Saint Peter's. For one thing, France was using his power for her own aggrandizement. For another, Guelf and Ghibelline without his leadership were ever at each other's throats. But the heart-searing fact of this present exile was that it was voluntary, self-imposed.

Suddenly with a gesture of command, Catherine cried: "We must work. We must pray. Let no one rest until the Vicar of Christ takes his place in Rome."

Wonderingly Alessa looked at her. For all her marvellous power over souls, did this girl of twenty-three believe she could influence the great Papal Court? Yet three months later when news came that Urban Fifth had died, Alessa learned the identity of his successor with new elation. Roger de Beaufort had been elected. He called himself Gregory Eleventh. "In this Pope we may have hope of action," she cried eagerly to Catherine. "He has ideals and enthusiasm."

Most of the Sienese, however, merely shrugged to learn of the new Pope's crowning. Since civic peace had been established they were too busy with trade and pleasure to give much thought to the future. Every occasion was made a pretext for feast and revel. For example, one February evening in 1371 the Sansedoni, a family of distinguished nobility, gathered together some three hundred guests to celebrate the coming of age of the youngest son. Their vast brick palace, which looks today almost as it did then, faces the Campo, built to follow its curve.

Within torches flared on the stairways and great fires roared on the hearthstones. In the magnificent central hall, tables were placed along the walls and servants ran about supplying the guests with plates of game and stuffed birds, with sweetmeats, cheese, wine and costly fruits. In a balcony above the host and hostess stood musicians playing lively airs. And beneath, in the open space between the tables, jesters in motley were singing and presenting humorous dances and acrobatics.

A late comer to the entertainment was ushered by a servant to the rear of the hall. There, far from the music, unaccompanied by any of the fair ladies in sparkling jewels whose presence graced the occasion, two gentlemen sat in talk. Before them the newcomer paused and signalled to the servant that he would sit beside them.

Swiftly the elder of the two men sprang from his seat. "Greetings, Andrea Vanni!" he cried. "Why are you so late? Do you expect roast goose at this hour?"

Vanni replied laughing, "There ought to be plenty of goose where there is so much cackling!" Then to his friend's companion he said, "Good evening to you, Messer Ranieri di Landoccio! I remember our meeting many years ago at the house of Francesco Malavolti. Why are you and Cristofano di Gano not laughing at the buffoons? Come, tell me the subject of your discourse."

Neri smiled apologetically. "I confess we are serious. We speak of the new Pope's need of reforming the abuses of the Church. Messer di Gano is full of hope. But I am of a melancholy turn and think little will be done from Avignon."

Vanni had seated himself. Lifting a goblet of wine which a page had placed before him, he said

soberly: "You asked, Cristofano, why I was late.
Until the light failed, I was painting a polyptych
commanded for the church of San Stefano. When I
looked at my Virgin and Bambino I thought of the
fat priest who would celebrate the Mass before
them and of all the rich Cardinals who set the example of selfishness on the banks of the Rhone. I
forgot this feast in my desire to see on earth one
example of more than common goodness, one face
touched by God."

Neri di Landoccio's eyes kindled at the passion
in the man's voice. He had regretted that upon entering the palace he had been seized and borne off
by Messer di Gano. The good notary, whose invitation to this gathering was due to his having tutored
two of the Sansedoni, had snatched at his young
friend as one of the few he knew. But now Neri
felt that a talk with Andrea Vanni was worth all
the frivolity he was missing.

Gano had followed his friend's words with em-
phatic nods. Suddenly, however, his eyes dilated
with another interest. "*Ecco!*" he cried. "There
across the room is a beautiful face—albeit worldly
enough. Look at that young girl in robe of velvet
rose sitting by a cavalier in blue. Does she not please
Messer Vanni, the artist?"

Both men followed the direction of his outflung
hand. Then Andrea said: "*Per Bacco!* That is the
young wife of Francesco Malavolti. She is truly of
rare sweetness. And she has need of it. Her light-
hearted husband there beside her cannot be faithful
to one woman—be she ever so lovely."

"Not he," laughed Neri. "Yet Francesco is far from evil. Yesterday morning I found him earnestly reading a Greek Gospel. Were his imagination but deeply touched I think he would serve goodness well."

Vanni looked at the speaker with friendly eyes. "He read to me one of your poems lately. You acquire fame with your verse. Have you long returned from your studies at Perugia?"

"Not long," said Neri, confused at the praise. "I missed the great fight against the Salimbeni."

At that moment a fanfare of trumpets shattered the talk and laughter of the hall. A herald in green and gold announced that there would be dancing among the guests. Immediately retainers began to carry out the serving tables in the center. The guests arose. Music sounded from the balcony and Messer Sansedoni, the host, passed from one group to another to urge on the dancing.

Resigning themselves to the inevitable, the three friends separated. Neri had hardly taken a dozen steps down the room when he heard his name called. In an instant he was clasping hands with Stefano Maconi.

"It is good fortune to see you once again," said the latter bending his frank, cordial gaze upon Neri. "You have changed much in these seven years. I fear you have studied too diligently. A melancholy shadow lives in your eyes."

Flushing, Neri replied: "And you? Have you vanquished all your enemies?"

Stefano laughed. "Oh, there is always some

quarrel to be taken up. But, tell me, what are you doing here in Siena?"

Neri's thin, dark face took on a wry smile. "I go to *fiestas* such as this. I read and see my friends. I go to the University to hear lectures by the Dominican, Fra Bartolommeo. I have settled upon nothing. Truly I find everything tedious."

"Exactly that did Francesco Malavolti say to-night. He declared he was weary of amusing himself. It would seem that neither in books nor in love is satisfaction to be found. Perhaps I am wise to hunt and fight and have no time for sadness. By your leave," he broke off, "I see a lady yonder who might tread with me this roundelay." With a bow he was off.

A moment later Neri, too, found himself a charming partner. And for a time in the gaiety of movement and laughter he forgot his habitual brooding. Yet before the evening came to an end moodiness was upon him again. The room with its hundreds of candles and its shifting figures in gorgeous fabrics swam before his eyes. He thought it like a richly wrought goblet full of insipid wine. Suddenly he found his friend Francesco Malavolti beside him and checking the latter's gay greeting, he laid a hand upon his arm.

"Do me a favour, friend. A wish has come upon me to rest my eyes on a thing with Heaven in it. A moon shines bright outside. Come with me for a look at the Duomo."

Francesco stared. "Are you mad, Neri? Leave the ball now?"

"COME WITH ME FOR A LOOK AT THE DUOMO"

"Yes, I am a little mad. Come, indulge my fancy. You can return to your whispered intrigue within half the hour."

Francesco's brilliant blue eyes danced. Any wild notion found favour with him. The slight risk to two gentlemen wandering about the streets alone made him yield to his companion's wish. Soon, wrapped in their fur-lined cloaks, they set forth.

Outside the Sansedoni palace they paused an instant to watch the late moon over the arrowy tower of the Signoria. Then, skirting the Campo, they passed up the street beside the Podestà's house and turned into the via dei Pellegrini. Pitch black was the narrow way and thick the snow beneath their feet.

Francesco, humming an air beneath his breath, laid a hand on Neri's shoulder. "What would your poet Dante, who walked this very street before our time, say of this expedition?"

Neri, his spirits risen, answered gaily, "He'd think ill of *you* in any case. You belong to the *Brigata Spendereccia*—the spendthrift youth he scorned."

As they emerged into the little square about San Giovanni, the Baptistery, they looked upwards. But the moon was now hidden under dark, racing clouds. The place was folded deep in shadow and all at once the snow began to fall. Francesco was about to curse his friend for dragging him out to no purpose when Neri caught his arm.

"Look! Who descends there?"

Both men gazed up the long steep flight of steps

leading from the Baptistery to the piazza of the cathedral. Through the blackness a little light wavered on the stairway and cast a feeble glow into the snowy air. Down it came a step or two. What late wanderer could be passing at this hour? Moved by curiosity, each man made a simultaneous gesture to the other to wait and see.

Suddenly in the weighted stillness came a little cry. The light flickered and sank. For an instant there was no further movement from it. Francesco whispered: "The knave has fallen. A sober head is needed for those steps in snow."

But now the light was coming down again. Presently, to their amazement, appeared, dimly illumined in the lantern rays, the figure of a woman. Black cloak and white robe indicated a Mantellata. Wearily the figure halted. The small lamp was held high to show the way. In its beam shone a face, delicate and worn for all its youth, such a face as neither of the watchers had ever looked upon. Breathless they saw upon the white swathing of her head a bright spot of blood. Her dark eyes, not seeing her observers, gazed left and right. Then with a little smile of recognition she passed down the street toward Fonte Branda.

Transfixed by the strange beauty of that vision, the two young men stood motionless until she was swallowed in the gloom. Then Francesco gasped. "She bruised her head upon those cursed steps. We should follow that no ill happen to her. *Dio!* Who could she have been?"

Neri made no move to accept his friend's suggestion. An unknown exultation filled his heart. For some instants he was speechless. Then he uttered in an awed murmur, "I have seen it—I have seen it!"

"What?" cried Francesco, shaking him half angrily. "Who was that angelic being?"

"That I know not. Likely a Mantellata come from nursing at the Scala. But I do know this. I have seen the face that Vanni wished to paint—one lighted by Divinity."

With one accord the two retraced their steps in silence. No need to climb upward for a view of the cathedral. Already they had found what they had sought—a glimpse of unearthly loveliness.

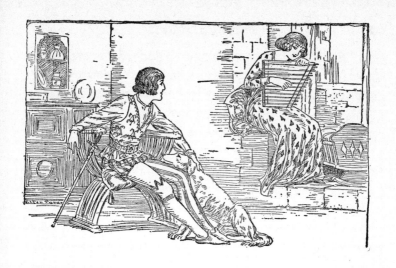

Chapter Four

WITH his long legs and pointed shoes stretched out before him, Francesco Malavolti sat playing with his greyhound. Through oiled parchment which covered tall windows at his left the morning sun poured into the sumptuous apartment. Since his marriage the young man lived on the third floor of the family palace. Across the room on the high window-seat sat his wife—not yet eighteen. At her feet was a wooden cradle in which a baby slept. In her hands she held a psaltery and as she strummed it she chanted softly a melancholy air.

Swiftly Francesco rose and went over to her. Standing on the broad step below the embrasure of the window, he leaned to kiss the soft, curving cheek. "My sweet!" he murmured. "Art thou happy?"

With a tremulous flutter of white eyelids, the young woman dropped her head. Softly she answered, "I could be happy, my husband, didst thou but love me more truly."

Tenderly the man gazed into the fair face. "I do love thee, *cara*. Truly I know not why I ever wander from thy side. I am restless, too easily tempted."

Flushing, the girl raised her head and there was conflict in her sombre eyes. Then she said passionately: "Would some influence on God's earth might make thee more stable! Were I a man and not mewed up with cares of children and the house, I should think of something besides pleasure!"

Deeply startled, he stared at the accusing face. But before he could reply the portière at the entrance into the hallway was brusquely pushed aside. With every air of haste two women entered. One of them was Francesco's mother and the other, Madonna Giovanna, wife of Currado Maconi. In their preoccupation, they scarcely received the formal greetings from the young people.

Abruptly Madonna Giovanna exclaimed, "Have you twain heard of the fear and sorrow suffered this day by the family of the Bellanti?"

In surprise Francesco said, "You speak of the family of young Andrea?"

"Ah," cried his mother, "that youth came into the world only to grieve his parents. He was rich and well instructed. Yet did he give his days to wine and all the pleasures of the flesh."

"Yes," chimed in Francesco's wife, "they say he

even throws dice with the rabble of Siena on the Campo. What has he done now?"

"*Oimè!* Now it is what he will *not* do," returned Madonna Giovanna. "He lies on his bed of death, refusing to repent or confess his sins. They sent for a parish priest and Andrea only blasphemed. Then they sent for Father della Fonte of San Domenico, but to no purpose. The poor mother! Her son faces eternal damnation in hell. Were my Stefano in such peril—dear, good youth that he is, thank God—I should go mad."

Francesco looked perturbed. "But is Andrea sure to die?"

"They said he could not live through the night. I have sent a page to inquire if he showed no change of heart before it was too late. We await the answer now."

Even as she spoke there came the sound of feet on the stairs and a panting servant entered the room. "A miracle!" he gasped. "Messer Andrea has died a Christian! Toward midnight he called for a priest, repented all his sins and accepted the Blessed Sacrament."

"Praised be God!" cried Madonna Giovanna. "What moved his stubborn heart?"

"A miracle, madonna," repeated the servant in a tone of awe. "Even as he felt the Devil seizing his soul to bear it off to torment a virgin came to intercede and so wrought upon his spirit that all his wickedness fell from him on the instant. Forthwith he sent for a priest and told him what I tell you."

"A virgin?" echoed Francesco's mother, looking about at the amazed faces.

"Yes, madonna. The street is full of people talking of the miracle. It was she of Fonte Branda— Catherine, the Mantellata. Last night Father della Fonte went to the maid Catherine and begged her to pray for the dying sinner and it was she brought him to grace. By prayer alone! She came not near him in the flesh."

"But who is this virgin of Fonte Branda?" asked Francesco's wife.

"Already have I heard of her," replied Madonna Giovanna. "She has done much good for the poor and the sick. They say at prayer in San Domenico she is translated to Heaven and knows nothing that happens about her."

"Oh, how could it be?" cried out the girl. "To move not from her chamber and convert that head-strong sinner by prayer alone! Dost thou believe this, Francesco?"

A curious expression, reverent, uplifted was stamped upon his careless face. "Yes," he said in a low voice, "I think I have seen this Catherine. To her all things would be possible." With a sudden movement as of escape, he bowed to the three women and left the room. He longed to be alone.

That desire was not easily fulfilled in those days. Despite the vast size of palaces and even houses, privacy was at a premium. What with all the married sons living under the same roof as their parents, what with the rooms always overflowing with children and servants and guests, life was one press of personalities. Meditative individuals and those faced by some crisis of the spirit found this sociable confusion a great hardship. But no one else comprehended any need for solitude. Consequently it was with bewilderment that Francesco's wife and his mother watched him flee their presence.

There was one woman in Siena, however, who would have understood his mood. This was she whose intense projection of the soul had so deeply affected the young Bellanti. Only in complete isolation, won through bitter struggle, could Catherine Benincasa gather up the power she had just demonstrated to all Siena. Father della Fonte made it his business to relate proof of her intercession. He told everyone how Catherine, who did not even know the Bellanti house by sight, was able to describe in minute detail the bedroom in which the dying sinner had lain.

But only so desperate a case evoked from her deliberate interference. Deeply as she yearned over human beings, she attempted only to persuade them toward the love of God. Her patience in dealing with a relative of Alessa Saracini astounded that young woman. Day after day, at her friend's insistence that she save the renegade, Catherine sat by Francesco Saracini's hearthstone. Unprotesting she let the bitter old man rave against the Church and everyone in it—particularly a certain Prior with whom he had quarrelled. She spoke only of Him on whom the Church was founded. And gradually she brought a glorious image of Truth to life before Francesco's eyes.

One day he found his resistance melted away and in its place a longing to worship. Turning suddenly to Catherine, he said, "I am ready to do anything you say."

Laughing joyously, the girl held out to him both hands and said in a loving tone, "Go quickly, and make peace with your enemy and thence to confession."

What happened then made good telling around the flasks of Chianti in all the great palaces of the city. Many had observed the fighting, hunting, swearing old nobleman the morning he left his house at Catherine's bidding. Many had met him as he laboured on the arm of a servant up to the cathedral. He bore upon his wrist his favourite falcon— a gentleman's gift made in amends to an enemy. Therefore they knew he was seeking out the hated Prior. Afterwards they learned that the Prior when summoned did not wait to observe the peace offering. He took one look at Saracini and fled for his life. Only with the utmost difficulty was the priest persuaded his visitor had come to prove his repentance.

So far the tale was merry enough. But its conclusion checked the laughter of listeners. For now Messer Francesco went to Mass each day. That hatred-starved old face was filled with happiness and the grasping, wrinkled claw opened wide to distribute alms to the poor.

When it was asked who had wrought this marvellous change in the old heretic, the narrator would answer: "Catherine, the dyer's daughter of Fonte

Branda. They say no one can resist her efforts in behalf of God. Lately she has talked to the women of the Tolomei. That wolf Giacomo, the son and brother, rages at this threat to his ambition. He strives to marry off his young sisters to wealthy husbands. But wait and see! He, too, may yield to this Catherine's persuasion."

It was Monna Raba, a truly religious woman, who summoned the young Mantellata to the Tolomei palace. One of her sons, Matteo, was inclined to the Dominican Order. But her two lovely young daughters were being prepared by the tyrannous Giacomo for the marriage market. When Catherine in her austere simplicity entered the great room of the palace, the two girls blushed under their paint and powder to receive her in their costly clothes and jewels.

Sweetly Catherine talked to them in a way that gave courage to their timid hearts. And when she left, the painted dolls rose up defiantly. They stripped off their trappings and from then on refused to bleach their hair or use cosmetics. In vain Giacomo stormed and tore from their hands copies of Holy Writ. His mother made him receive Catherine and in the clear mirror of her eyes he had to see his tyranny as it was. Thereupon he not only ceased to dominate his sisters, but himself changed his ways and became a good and pious citizen. His transformation was one more marvel for Siena to recount.

To Alessa and to Cecca Gori, however, no instance of Catherine's persuasiveness was so impressive as the change she wrought in her own mother. Lapa who once resented the character of her unwed daughter's life now followed her about with a humility both funny and touching. She worried constantly over the girl's physical frailty. This was due to the strain of her intense inner life. For many days she sometimes remained in a state of ecstasy which entirely cut off the world about her. In that condition she could take no food and was left weak and suffering.

"Caterina kills herself for others," Lapa used to grumble to Lisa, her daughter-in-law. "If it is not at the hospitals she labours then it is at converting sinners who had best go to the Devil in any case. Would she had never donned that black mantle and white robe!"

Yet the day came when Lapa herself put on the costume of the Tertiaries. She fell desperately ill and promised Catherine, who hovered beside her day and night, that if her life were spared she would become a Mantellata. When she recovered her daughter joyously held her to her word and welcomed her into the fold.

A special reason for Lapa's increased dependence upon Catherine was the metamorphosis in the life of the Benincasa family. The three brothers, especially since Bartolommeo's unlucky alliance with the Salimbeni, had not prospered in the dyeing business. They decided that in Florence, free from political entanglements, they would do better. In 1370 they had applied for citizenship papers to the

Florentine Republic and early the next year they moved their families and their chattels to that city.

This separation from her brothers and their children had a potent effect on Catherine's career. For her longing to keep in touch with them inspired her to think of sending them frequent letters. She herself could not write. But Alessa, who could read and write both Latin and Italian, offered to take her dictation. Catherine found this mode of expression singularly easy. She sent missives also to Father Lazzarino. That learned man, who had fled to an hermitage in Pisa for his soul's good wrote to ask her guidance and comfort in his loneliness. Thus began a new activity which rapidly drew the girl into the great currents of her age.

Already she was at the very centre of Siena's flowing life. Now the most ardent among the hundreds of people who knew her began to form a definite group about her. This centrifugal movement began with a single individual.

Impressed by the melancholy thoughtfulness of one of his young friends at the University, Father Bartolommeo invited him to meet Catherine Benincasa. The youth, to whom the name meant nothing, indifferently assented and accompanied the priest one afternoon to the house of Alessa Saracini. Already a number of the Mantellate and several Dominicans were gathered there and the sound of talk and laughter greeted the newcomer's ears. He bowed low before Alessa whose name he knew well and then was brought to a small figure in the centre of the group. He heard some one say, "This is Messer Ranieri di Landoccio dei Pagliaresi."

What else was said he did not know. His heart was pounding with the wonder of his discovery. That face, those marvellous dark eyes, the smile which seemed an inner light—these he had seen before. This was she whom Francesco and he had glimpsed one snowy night when she had fallen on the steps beside the Baptistery. Unable to speak, Neri listened to the music of her rapid Tuscan, stole glances at her radiant face and hugged close his felicity. When he left the house it was with one idea —to return.

Neri's diffidence made him write to ask permission for another visit. The answer came with surprising promptness, delivered by a small boy who said with pride that he was Catherine's nephew. Hastily breaking the seals, Neri read this missive, penned in the hand of Alessa Saracini.

You asked me to receive you as a son: wherefore I, though miserably unworthy, have already received you and do now receive you with affectionate love and I hold myself responsible, and will ever do so before God, to pay your debts for every sin committed, or which you may commit. But I beseech you to fulfil my desires; confirm yourself with Christ Crucified and cut yourself off completely from the conversation of the world.

His subsequent visit inspired Neri's admiration anew. This woman was not only angelic, but wise and eloquent. She had a robust sense of the heroic adventure of goodness. This time when he parted from her his shy desire was put into words. "Is there a service on this earth that I could render you?"

A look of happy gratitude sprang into Catherine's face. Then with rising colour, she asked with something of his own timidity: "Could you write letters for me? I receive increasing numbers every day. My poor Alessa cannot write them all and it grieves me to send no word to anxious hearts. Often the messengers must wait many hours for my answer."

Joyously Neri began his work as secretary. To take Catherine's dictation was to discover that she was a poet. He loved her rich imagery. His face would glow to set down such a phrase as, "We must perceive among the thorns the perfume of the flower about to open." He marvelled at her ability to make the most tiresome virtues alluring. "Oh, Patience," she apostrophized in one letter, "thy garment is of the sun, shining with the light of true knowledge of God."

Neri's pen raced to follow that rapid flow of words. And when they ceased he would raise a face lit up by enthusiasm. Often Catherine walked up and down as she dictated, the gestures of her strong, slender hands emphasizing her meaning. Then, as she finished, she would bend upon him that irradiating smile. "You write more swiftly than my dear Alessa," she would say gratefully.

Eagerly the young man flung himself into the task. He found addresses, engaged couriers for the letters, supplied the parchments and the seals. To set out for Fonte Branda each day was to feel every

mist of disenchantment and uncertainty lift from
his heart. At last he had found something in Siena
more fascinating than either dry learning or sensu-
ous enjoyment.

After several months of this absorbing occupa-
tion, he returned home one afternoon to find a
familiar figure pacing the courtyard of his house.
It was Francesco Malavolti.

"*Ecco!* At last you come!" cried the visitor. "It
is long since I have seen your face. Never a revel do
you grace these days. What occupies you and gives
you that sleek look of satisfaction?"

Neri hesitated, his eyes fixing that merry face.
He was surprised to find how little he wished to
converse with his friend. Francesco, however, had
his own interpretation of the other's mood.

"You have fallen in love!" he accused Neri in
high glee. "And I also! Come, confidence for confidence! At last I have found the woman of my
dreams, *mio caro*—tall, luscious as a ripe peach!
Today I sent her a chain of silver to signify my
wish to make her captive." With swaggering elbow,
he pushed back his wine-coloured cloak. "Now tell
me quickly who has caught your fancy!"

Not at once did Neri speak of his new mission in
life. But when he did so he begged Francesco to go
with him to see Catherine Benincasa. Malavolti
ceased his mocking the instant he heard that name,
but laughed away the invitation. What would he be
doing among the mystics? It was all right for a poet,
but as for him, he loved the stolen sweets of life too
well to give them up for serious pursuits. In the end,

however, purely out of friendship, he agreed to go to Fonte Branda.

"Do not imagine, though," he said, "that I shall change my life for your holy maid. Nor will I confess my little sins."

Two days later Neri presented his friend to Catherine. He watched Francesco closely. When the blue eyes met that searching gaze, the gay face grew pale as death. The debonair manner dropped away and the clever tongue was still. As if his head were reeling, the young man sank into a seat.

He had been received in a warm, loving way, universal as sunshine. Now in silence he listened as Catherine discoursed with Fra Bartolommeo and the others. In amazement, he who had so often yawned at sermons realized that he was not being preached at. He was being gathered in to share a glowing, vital life. For the first time he felt that the world of the spirit was true. As he left the circle with Neri, he did not utter a single word. But at the top of Costa San Antonio he stopped and with a nod of farewell and a pressure of the hand, he turned toward Camporeggi.

"Where do you go?" asked Neri in astonishment.

Francesco's eyes, glancing back, showed the glitter of tears. "To confess my black sins at San Domenico," he muttered solemnly.

In his whole-hearted fashion young Malavolti became at once a member of Catherine's followers. He helped Neri with the ever-increasing correspondence and took delight in bringing his friends to Fonte Branda. Patiently he endured the ribald baiting of the young blades whose society he had promptly quitted and even chuckled with them at the overturning of his own boast to remain immune from holy blandishments.

There was one man, however, who needed no persuasion to join the rapidly growing circle. Later in his *Memoires* this individual set down these words

And in this time when I commenced to be in Siena God drew outside into the world a new star, full of the Holy Spirit. It was the reverenced Caterina, blessed and holy and very holy and most blessed, who was called Caterina di Monna Lapa of Fonte Branda, Mantellata of Camporeggi. To whom by means of Neri di Landoccio, her spiritual son, I was taken and so I could hear of those ties of God which do not let men go and such a woman one would not have believed to have heard. For certainly in her God renewed the Holy Spirit.

Thus did Messer Cristofano di Gano Guidini, the notary, introduce his account of a relationship which meant more to him than any other in his life.

It was he who brought to Catherine his most admired friend, Andrea Vanni. After the presentation Cristofano drew the artist aside and said to him, "Do you remember a wish you once made? If so, tell me, has it not come true?"

Andrea's dreamy eyes remained fixed on Catherine's face as he replied. "*Si, si,* I remember. She has, indeed, a divine beauty. There is the aloofness of one who lives partly in Heaven and the compassion of one who loves all human beings."

"Promise me that you will paint the blessed

Caterina some day!" cried the notary in his insistent fashion. Nor would he let him go until Vanni had consented.

There were, of course, many men connected with the Church in this unique assemblage. One of them, a young Dominican novice, was so shy that Catherine had to reassure him constantly with special attention. Matteo Cenni, rector of the Misericordia, came whenever he had time and those two old friends, Tommaso della Fonte and Father Bartolommeo, were always bringing visitors and distinguished acquaintances.

One day when Catherine was conversing with her friends she broke off abruptly and uttered a gay laugh. "Now in a moment," she said, "you will see something happen. Two big fish will fall into the net."

Even at her last words there came a knock upon the door. Shortly after an impressive entrance was made by two dignitaries. One proved to be the Franciscan Provincial and the other Father Tantucci, an Augustinian scholar of great repute. Received by Catherine with deferential warmth, they seated themselves on each side of her and without preliminary began disdainfully to catechize her about theology.

"Is man predestined toward good or evil or has he free will?" asked one.

"Does a good man go to Heaven whether or not he joins the Church?" demanded the other.

With humility and wisdom Catherine answered these formal inquiries. But the assembled auditors felt what Francesco Malavolti expressed in an indignant murmur to Neri. "These learned men have come here only to set a trap for our blessed mother and bring her to naught."

At last the witness turned upon her questioners with a grave air of authority. "Learned fathers, in this science of doctrine you present but the shell of Christianity. Doth not its kernel lie rather in the manner of one's life, in serving others?"

A profound silence followed. Neri who had visited the Provincial at his monastery knew these words must have struck him to the heart. He lived with lordly luxury, not in a cell, but in a vast apartment filled with handsome furniture and costly ornaments. Nor was he ever known to bestir himself in behalf of anyone on earth. Catherine's challenge like a bright sword cleaved through dry argument straight to the roots of religion. Before all that company rose up a vision of the Galilean healing the sick and preaching to the poor.

Confusion drove from the faces of the two theologians their haughty assurance. Suddenly the Provincial rose and with a violent gesture as if he cast off a burden grown intolerable, he snatched from his pouch a bunch of keys. Flinging it at two young men seated in a corner, he cried out, "For the love of God, go to my room and distribute all that is in it and leave me nothing but my Breviary."

It was said with the magnificent simplicity characteristic of those days. Instantly the hostility felt by every member of the group toward the visitors was melted. Cordially they pressed about the great doctors and drew them into the loving fellowship of Catherine's circle. Here, where there was no will to shine nor succeed and consequently no malice nor jealousy, a peculiarly joyous spirit prevailed. These men and women felt themselves members of one huge family. And whereas all others used the title of "mother" when they spoke to Catherine, they chose a more intimate term to express a blend of awe and affection. They called her "Mamma." Grey-haired scholars, grandmothers, young men of her own age—all addressed this girl of twenty-five by that name.

When Francesco Malavolti first heard Cristofano di Gano, the pompous middle-aged notary, call Catherine "*Mamma mia*" he shook with ill-repressed laughter. But such anomalies were part of the happiness in which the family basked. Neri would never have dreamed that the cultivated and the erudite would flock to Fonte Branda. Alessa had supposed other members of the nobility would scorn to follow a tradesman's daughter. Malavolti with amazement found himself feeling close kinship with the son of a traditional family enemy. This was Matteo Tolomei, brother of that fierce Giacomo whom Catherine had tamed.

One of Catherine's closest friends never came to her house. On the contrary she and her companions went to visit him. He was a hermit who dwelt some distance from Siena. Just below the hill on which stood an Augustinian monastery in a thick grove of oaks beside a little lake, this man spent every day in his retreat. At night he mounted the hill to his monastic cell. So much in love with loneliness was he that he disliked even to assist at Mass once a week.

Almost as soon as she had become friends with Matteo Cenni of the Mercy Hospital Catherine had heard of this man. "You must visit the Bachelor," Matteo would say. "That holy hermit converted me from a life of sin and selfishness." He explained that this was an Englishman by the name of William Flete who had his title by virtue of being a Bachelor of Arts at Oxford before settling in Italy.

One day a little company escorted Catherine out to visit the hermit of Lecceto—Alessa Saracini, Cecca Gori, the rector of the Misericordia and Father Tantucci, the Augustinian scholar whom Catherine had so recently converted from critic to friend. He himself was called Master because of his advanced degree. It was while he was taking it at Oxford that he had met William Flete. Tantucci assured Catherine that the Bachelor's learning, sincerity and devotion to his friends more than atoned for all his oddities.

The pilgrimage was a gay interlude in the lives of these busy folk. Flowers along the streams, birds in the thick dark woods, the blue of distant hills—all that she loved in Nature set Catherine to singing and praising God. Her reception by William Flete touched her heart. Clothed in his brown habit, he came forth from his retreat to greet the visitors. "I have heard much of you from many holy men," said he to Catherine. His penetrating eyes seemed to pierce her very soul and recognize it for a shrine. They talked as if they had known each other for years.

Toward evening the Bachelor escorted his guests through the wood to the monastery gate. A watch tower and lofty wall about the place testified to the need felt even by monks for protection against robber bands. In the courtyard was a stone well and a vegetable garden weeded carefully. Cloisters framed the little plot.

With an ironic smile the hermit pointed out the frescoes on the cloister walls. "There," said he, "you will find every trick the Devil plays pictured in lively scenes. Look at them and you will not miss Siena."

Supper was served the company in a square room, empty except for benches and the table. Across the hall they could see the Brothers at their meal. The silence preserved by the monks on all days except Sunday was broken by the voice of a friar seated in a small balcony. He read from the Scriptures as the others ate. Catherine learned the reader's name —Filippo degli Agazzari. But not for many years, when he was old, was this man distinguished for anything but piety. Then he dipped a pen in vitriol and wrote an impassioned denunciation of human folly. Conceived in the same spirit of Paolo Neri's frescoes in the cloisters, these *Examples* written by the old Prior have been handed down to this day. They portray with marvellous vividness the Devil's masterful alacrity in a scandalous age.

On that May evening, however, as Catherine communed with the hermit, as the nightingale sang softly in the dark and the breeze wafted in fragrance of *ginestra* and honeysuckle, the quiet monastery held no hint but of beauty and peace. After her first visit to Lecceto, Catherine often went there with her companions and despite frequent disagreements, she and William Flete became warm friends.

One feature of that monastery life reminded Alessa of the circle in Fonte Branda. For Catherine often read to the members during supper. To foregather at the hour of repast suited people so strenuously occupied and they loved its sociability. To share it Catherine would nibble a bit of lettuce or a crust of bread moistened in wine. Yet even this nourishment gave her acute discomfort and she could seldom retain it in her stomach. Nobody could imagine how her marvellous energy was sustained merely on water and the juice of vegetables. But her companions accepted the phenomenon as they did her lapses from usual consciousness. Strangers, of course, were curious and suspicious and this attitude gave Catherine great pain. She hated to have her own peculiarities detract anyone's attention from vital matters.

In the year 1372 such issues were at stake. A tremendous ideal had suddenly been lifted before the eyes of Christendom by the new Pope, Gregory Eleventh. Almost his first act was to prepare the way for a Crusade. Throughout the centuries there had been five of these expeditions against the Turks and over a million Christians had perished in Asia Minor. The last attempt to conquer Jerusalem and stem Mohammedan power had been made by Saint

Louis, King of France. But that was now a hundred years ago and since then every gain had been lost. The Christian Emperor of the East was in the Sultan's power and Hungary was in peril from the infidels.

To rouse all nations to a sense of religious obligation and racial danger Gregory Eleventh had the Crusade preached everywhere. He sent special letters to the King of England, the Count of Flanders and the Doge of Venice. Each was urged to raise forces to attack the foes of the Christian world. To the Grand Master of the Knights of Rhodes he gave Smyrna to be used as an Eastern rendezvous for armies of every country.

It was easy to stir men of imagination. That mysticism inherited from the Middle Ages caused the dream of following the fiery Cross into battle to appeal alike to warrior and saint, to knight and retainer. Men too practical for such a vision were capable of fearing the advance of Mohammedan hordes. Consequently in the wake of Gregory's propaganda a wave of interest spread little by little to every corner of Europe.

With pæans of rejoicing Catherine Benincasa received news of the Crusade. She took it as a challenge to the Church to shake off her sloth and undergo hardship for the right. A united Italy, a united Christendom, peace won through a holy war —such were the majestic conceptions which filled her mind. She talked and wrote of nothing else.

Catherine's wide contacts through conversations and letters had made her fully conversant with the menacing situation faced by the Church. Resentment of the fact that the Pope himself was a Frenchman burst into open antagonism against the French Legates who controlled certain territories of the Church and who wished to increase their sway in other cities. Instead of trying to conciliate this opposition, the Papal representatives went to any lengths to combat it. Cardinal Gérard du Puy, Governor of Perugia, for example, deliberately aroused a quarrel between two of the Republics and secretly treated with the outlaw, Cione Salimbeni, to fight against Siena. Later the Cardinal at Bologna engaged the bloodthirsty John Hawkwood and his mercenaries to undertake a campaign of destruction in Tuscany.

Pierre d'Estaing, the Papal Legate at Bologna, did nothing to control the growing fury between Church and nation. Consequently oppression from the representatives of Gregory made Italians feel that the Church was an enemy of liberty. Rebellion against Papal authority was becoming synonymous with patriotism.

This ghastly situation which puzzled so many minds seemed to the young woman of Siena quite clear of solution. Were churchmen to demand less temporal power they would command more spiritual obedience. Were the Pope to return to Rome he would free the Church from French domination and restore to it its universal character of Christendom. Because she felt national hatreds would go down before an international Christian movement, she flung herself into the support of the Crusade.

Let men of all lands but fight shoulder to shoulder for the defence of their religion and local antagonisms would cease.

Moved by such convictions, she wrote a magnificent letter to Pierre d'Estaing. Calling upon him to preach and live the gospel of love, she said: "Make peace—if it is possible. It is a shame to see you with arms in your hands fighting one against the other instead of all faithful Christians fighting against the infidels."

In the same spirit, she dictated a response to the unscrupulous plotter at Perugia, Cardinal du Puy. Having got into difficulties in his relations with Siena, he had sent a conciliatory letter to the one citizen he thought powerful enough to help him—Catherine Benincasa. Now this man, as the girl well knew, was the Pope's nephew and would doubtless send her reply to Gregory. Yet with utter fearlessness she told him exactly what she thought.'

It is well known that two single things, through which the Bride of Christ is being destroyed, must be done away with. One is the too great tenderness and solicitude among relatives. . . . The other is too great softness based upon too great mercy. . . . I, your poor little daughter, take upon me all your sins and thus mine and yours shall burn together in the fire of mercy. . . . Work with the Holy Father and exert all force to chase from the fold those wolves, those demons incarnate among the shepherds who attend to nothing if not to eating, to beautiful palaces and fat horses.

Echoes of such plain talk resounded far and wide in the ecclesiastical world. They were borne on the winds Catherine stirred to blow men's hearts hot for the Crusade. One result of this agitation was a new recruit to her circle—Don Giovanni of the Cells, a renowned penitent of enormous influence. Spreading broadcast his enthusiasm, he wrote of her, "Oh, angelic and divine, she illuminates our hemisphere like the sun."

Such an expression was typical of the attention now focused upon the young Dominican by churchmen of every degree in all parts of the land. Recognition from another lofty quarter of Italy followed immediately.

One day the urchins in the dingy Quarter of the Goose stopped their play to stare at an approaching stranger. They had never seen anyone so grand— cloak of green and scarlet doublet, long tights with one leg white and the other orange, two retainers in scarlet mantles buttoned to the ankles! Curiously the youngsters watched to see if he could really be going where all the other visitors to Fonte Branda always went—to the house of Catherine Benincasa.

That was, indeed, the man's destination. He was the ambassador to Siena of Bernabo Visconti, the great lord of Milan. Visconti's house was immensely rich and powerful and he, unscrupulous and wolfish, carried on with the Pope the greatest single struggle in all Italy. Once he had had burned alive two friars who had protested against his barbarous treatment of his own people. For his defiance of the Papal Legates he had been excommunicated by Urban Fifth and now was attempting to win other cities to resist the Legates of Gregory Eleventh. Already he had agreed to join the league Florence was forming. Obviously Bernabo felt that were he to secure the sympathy of Catherine Benincasa his cause would prosper in Siena. It was an amazing tribute to her fame.

To that ardent being no human avenue to reform was unwelcome. She received the ambassador of Milan's tyrant with great cordiality. She wrote not only to Bernabo, but to his wife, the frivolous Beatrice della Scala. It was a peerless opportunity to tell them to repent their sins, to assure them that not by defiance, but by loving obedience would they right any wrongs between the Pope and his Italian subjects.

I tell you [she declared], that God does not wish you nor anyone else to make yourself the executive of His ministers for He has reserved this to Himself and committed it to his Vicar.

Her message to Bernabo closed with an eloquent appeal to support the Crusade.

With her acceptance of such relationships Catherine was from that time forward definitely involved in the politics of her time. Her alert intelligence absorbed from every possible source facts which illuminated the situation and the personalities involved in it. One of the most direct of those sources opened up to her unexpectedly.

Before the circle met one evening during the year 1373 Andrea Vanni presented himself. There was an excitement in his air, an unwonted keenness in his eyes which told her that he had news. "Little

Mamma," said he without wasting words, "I am to be sent by the Signoria as an ambassador to Avignon. The governors are much disturbed by the contention which threatens Siena itself and I am to plead with Il Papa to return to Rome."

Catherine's face glowed. "I agree. Only so will jealousy of France be set at rest. Once in Rome our Holy Father will recognize that his French ministers do but stir up revolt. The taxes they collect go to pay for the wars of the French king with England. Thus money is diverted from the Church Universal. My son, I rejoice that they have chosen thee. Thou wilt serve our people well."

Andrea leaned toward her. "Thou wouldst serve better, *Mamma mia*. But I shall tell thee all. It is for that I most delight to go."

Vanni was as good as his word. When he returned from his fruitless mission he held long conferences with Catherine and gave her an exact picture of the great Papal court in Provence. It was not one to cheer her heart. But to be discouraged was not in her. From the Communion service, from her daily prayers and meditations she drew too absolute a sense of the Divine power to overcome all obstacles for her ever to admit that the solution of this tremendous national problem was impossible.

No human contact available to her, however, could help her to form judgments or plan a course of action. It was she who from quite another plane of thinking gave inspiration and guidance to the members of her circle. They looked up to her with eyes dazzled by the scope of her influence. Often in the intimate gaiety of the supper hour they would remember with awe that this young woman sitting there had the ear of the most important men in Italy. Often Neri would put down the manuscript of Dante from which he read aloud evening after evening and would look at Catherine's absorbed face. "She understands all this ancient wisdom," he would think, "and she, if anyone, can use it for the world's good now."

It fell to Neri one May morning in 1374 to read to Catherine a communication just received. Its purport was so grave that he went at once to summon Father Bartolommeo and Fra Tommaso della Fonte. From San Domenico he went on to the Malavolti palace.

At the door of that young man's apartment Neri was escorted by a servant into the presence of Francesco's wife. Dressed in a wine-dark frock, looped up to show two petticoats of blue, the young woman was in the act of fitting a velvet cap upon her head. From the mirror of burnished silver on the wall she turned with a gracious smile to greet the visitor.

"Madonna," said Neri, raising her white fingers to his lips, "I meant not to trouble you. I seek your worthy husband."

"In a moment he will join us," she said smiling. "He dons fine raiment to match mine. We go to a christening of my new-born niece. Has Caterina Benincasa need of his services this morning?"

Neri hesitated. "There is important news to tell him."

"Good news, I hope," cried the young woman

anxiously. "Oh, the *beata* Caterina! I follow her with my prayers for the happiness she hath brought to this house. What a change she hath wrought in Francesco!"

"For the better, I trust!" cried a laughing voice and there stood her husband, regarding her with tender blue eyes. Then turning to Neri, he said, "Do you seek me for yourself or for our sweetest little Mamma?"

"There has happened a strange thing," returned the other quickly. "From the Master General of the Dominican Order a summons has come requiring our Mamma to repair to Florence to the General Chapter meeting. She believes she is to be tried for her shortcomings."

"What? That sinless dove!" cried Francesco hotly.

"But, *ecco*! Neither Fra Bartolommeo nor della Fonte denies the possibility. It is thought there has been much criticism of her living without food or sleep. Some believe she eats in secret and is a hypocrite. Also, her zeal for the Crusade has aroused protest in high places. She is a woman and young. The thing is unheard of."

"*Per Bacco!*" shouted his friend in dark anger. "How fervour and unworldliness are feared and hated in these wretched days!"

Neri laid a hand on his arm. "Do not approach this affair in wrath! Our dearest Mamma thinks and says it is the opening of a new path and she fears nothing so little on earth as questioning. If thus she might draw nearer to perfection, she would

be the more content. As for me, I know that who-
ever sees and hears her will be certain she is from
God."

For an instant the felicity of that conviction
shone in the three young faces. Then, with a low
bow to the lady, Neri said, "Let me stay your going
no longer. I did wish to set before you, Francesco,
the clear direction our thoughts must take in this
matter."

It was more than a fortnight after this when
Catherine started on her pilgrimage. Fra Tommaso
and Fra Bartolommeo had already departed. Because it was a full day's journey she set out from
the house at daybreak. Through the silent streets
the cavalcade passed with considerable commotion.
For, although only Alessa Saracini, Cecca Gori and
Lisa were accompanying Catherine to Florence, a
dozen people had come to escort them to the Porta
Camoillia.

Upon the sympathetic Neri devolved the necessity of comforting Monna Lapa. As if she were losing her daughter for ever she wailed at every step:
"But once before has Caterina quitted the city when
I took her to the cursed baths of Val d'Orcia. Now
she goes hence without me along fearsome roads
where cut-throats lurk. She goes to a trial by the
Order—she who has done no wrong in all her life
except to give too much to worthless folk—even
once her *mantello*! *Oimè!*"

Amused as he was, Neri envied his friend Francesco walking there ahead beside Catherine's mule
and receiving her last comments and commands.

When the procession reached the gate, however, he stepped close to the beloved little figure and for an instant held her hand in both his own.

Then Catherine turned the head of her mule and looked down upon the small company. In the clear light of early morning her pale face looked radiant with love and gratitude. "My children," she rang out sweetly, "may the blessing of God rest upon you. Fear nothing for my unworthy self and yield your hearts and your deeds to Jesus Christ now and always!"

A Dominican Brother uttered a short prayer for her safety. Monna Lapa rushed forward for one last embrace. Then all stood in silence to watch the four figures in their black cloaks set out along the dusty white road. Never before had they been separated from their "revered, joyous and sweetest Mamma." At any hour of day or night she had been ready to receive and comfort them. Now they had a sudden vision of the high purpose of that companionship. It was not meant to enclose them in a safe and happy shelter. It was a preparation for ever-expanding horizons of service. Matteo Cenni uttered the one wish in every heart.

"Give us courage to be strong in loneliness even as she is strong!"

Chapter Five

"OU are Messer Ranieri di Landoccio?"
A voice at the young man's elbow
startled him from his deep reverie. Me-
chanically he arose from his seat and
bowed to the figure standing before him in the
courtyard of his house. The stranger's garb pro-
claimed him a novice from San Domenico and in
his hand was a parchment, tied, but unsealed.

This the Dominican presented gravely. "Messer
Matteo Cenni of the Misericordia sends you this
missive to read. It came from Florence yesterday."

"From Florence?" Eagerness leaped into Neri's
face. "My thanks, Brother! Our dearest Mamma
sends it?"

"No, Messer Ranieri. It was written by Madonna
Alessa, but contains much news of Mother Cater-

ina." The messenger was staring closely at Neri. "We were certain you were ill. You are not?" Then, as the other muttered a denial, the novice added, "You will send the letter back this day—if you dare not venture forth?"

His tone was peculiar. But Neri in his impatience to be alone with the precious letter did not observe it. "*Sì, sì.* I shall visit Matteo this morning. Will you not rest here a moment? Even so early in the day the heat burns the skin."

Neri's courtesy, however, was tested no further. His visitor refused. And when he had been escorted to the outer court where a servant opened the door, Neri could return to his seat and with fervent fingers unroll the parchment.

In the month since Catherine's departure for Florence the young man had sunk back into the restless melancholy of former days. He had lost all sense of possessing the knowledge of God. Every form of the religious life seemed a hollow trap for the soul in doubt. Finally, he had given up all attempts to work at anything and for almost a week he had remained shut up in his house. There amid his dreams he could avoid the sickening heat, the sight of his fellow men, the sound of human futility. Now this parchment in his hands struck a ray of dazzling light into the dark recesses of his heart.

In the first place, Alessa told the fellowship— Neri's eyes sparkled to read—Catherine would return before the end of June. That meant in a few days! Moreover, the little Mamma's appearance before the Chapter had meant only that she had made new friends. No limitation had been placed on anything she wished to do. The only requirement made by the Order was that she accept for her confessor and guide Fra Raimondo delle Vigne da Capua. A learned man of great repute for sound practice and holy life, he had been head of the convent at Montepulciano and had already heard much of Caterina through Fra Tommaso who had visited him there. In Florence people had flocked to meet and talk with the *beata Caterina*. Now not only was she known to all the Dominican Order, but had a new following in the great city on the Arno. That summons had, indeed, proved a blessing and an opportunity—even as the little Mamma had predicted.

Neri rolled up the parchment and tied the silken cord. She was coming back! Joy rolled over him like a tide. But it was followed by the sense of deep remorse. He had not kept the faith in her absence. He had proved a weak reed to support her confidence. Leaping to his feet, he called a servant to bring him his peaked hat and his light *mantello*. He would go to the Misericordia on the instant.

Without obeying, the old servant stood regarding him with anxious eyes. "Do not go forth, Messer Neri. Here you are safe from threat of danger."

Scarcely hearing him, the young man snapped his fingers imperiously. "Hasten!" he cried. He panted to make up for lost time. How he wished some special service lay before him to accomplish before Catherine's return.

Through his absorption he noticed how reluctant

was the page to open for him the outer gate. But he thought the explanation lay in the well-meant wish to protect him from the heat. It struck his face like a blow and brought with it a sickening odour of decay which made his fastidious nostrils quiver with repugnance. But before he had gone far something happened which recalled the old servant's warning.

Some yards ahead the outer door of a tall house opened suddenly. In the dimness behind it Neri had the impression of some horrible action—a burly man seizing upon one more slender; a powerful, quick movement; then a crumpled figure in servant's tunic flying through the air and falling limp into the gutter. It was followed by a volley of oaths.

Horrified, Neri rushed forward. But at his first bound he was jerked back by a sinewy hand on his arm. He was in the grasp of a monk who had abruptly appeared beside him and was crying: "Young sir, touch him not. Court not the danger. Already the poor one is past aid."

"But why?" cried Neri, trying to wrest himself away. "Wickedly he hath been flung out of that house and is hurt in falling."

"I saw," replied the monk without relaxing his hold. "Fear doth ever lead to cruelty. Yet go no nearer, my son. It is useless. Already flies gather about the lips of the corpse." Deliberately Neri's captor faced him about toward a side street and gave him a vigorous push.

Dumbfounded and furious, Neri would have turned back defiantly. But at that moment there

came a great shouting and clatter of hoofs in the
street he faced and above the din he heard his name
shouted lustily. A black horse drew away from the
small cavalcade and stopped. The rider waved a
friendly hand and Neri saw bending down upon
him a familiar face.

"Ho, Messer Ranieri! Well met! Did you witness the fight? We have even now routed a band of
the cursed Rinaldini!" Glowing with triumph and
boyish zest Stefano Maconi leaned from his saddle.

In his surprise Neri forgot for an instant the
horror of a moment before. He looked up in silence.
The sight of this handsome horseman brought
something before him with startling vividness. It
was a sense of what a stream of experience had cut
him off from the bravado existence he used in some
degree to share with this lively fellow. It seemed
incredible that young Maconi should speak as if he
were still part of that trivial life.

"What ails you, Neri?" Stefano with a look of
anxiety had leaped down from the saddle. "You do
not feel ill, I hope? *Dio mio*, you should not be in
the city now! Have you a horse? Take mine and
leave! Go to Belcaro where Nanni di Ser Vanni receives refugees. Do not hesitate. Mount now and go
at once!"

Neri stared at him in profound amazement.
"Leave Siena?" he cried. "In the name of God,
why?"

Before Stefano could reply several things seemed
to happen at once in the incomprehensible street.
Not ten yards from the young men a servant carry-

ing a basket suddenly staggered and fell to the ground. Though onions and apples rolled from his basket in all directions he lay without further movement. At the same instant a woman came rushing from the house near which he lay. In her arms was an infant. Shrieking like one demented, she ran down the street and as she passed Neri saw that the baby's face was covered with black spots. Yet something still more arresting caught his starting eyes—an advancing procession of the Brothers of the Misericordia. In their black robes and caps, with torches in their hands they chanted prayers for the dead and as they moved rapidly along Neri saw that these familiar mourners bore not one bier, but five!

Dazedly he heard Stefano saying: "*Ecco!* Such are the reasons why you must not linger here. The danger is too great. You are not strong."

"But—Holy Virgin, what is it? What mean these horrors?"

"Neri! You know not? Where have you been? It is the plague, my friend! The plague has come upon us once again."

Neri's heart seemed to turn over in his body. So that was it! That was why people fell dead upon the street and no one went to aid them. That was why his servants tried to keep him home and Stefano offered him escape. Why had he not been told? A chill horror brought drops upon his brow. Death in its most hideous form stalked relentlessly here, omnivorous for victims.

The black horse shook his head and whinnied. Should he mount and fly? He felt Stefano's kind hand upon his arm. And then before his reeling senses there floated the memory of a face—beautiful, compassionate, austere. Would Catherine Benincasa have him save himself when others needed help?

Swiftly the blood rushed back into his cheeks. He found voice in his dry throat. "You are good, Stefano. I have not left my house for days and no one told me of the pestilence. But now have I work to do. Fear nothing for me. Have a care for yourself and a thousand thanks!" He clasped the young man's hand and hurried on.

He found his heart expanding strangely. For the first time since he had bade her farewell he felt Catherine close to him again. With firm step he hastened to the Ospedale della Misericordia. For an instant after entering the door, however, he had to cling for support to the back of a bench—so overpowering was the acrid odour of the place. Then resolutely he walked into the hall of the sick to find Matteo Cenni. Correct as ever in his black robe, mantle of lavender moiré and black biretta with white cheek bands, the rector was in the act of bathing the contorted body of a fresh victim. His worn face turned to Neri with a smile of welcome.

"I am here to help. Set me a task," murmured that young man and once again remorse smote him to the heart. How long he had remained in safety while his fellows struggled in the midst of awfulness!

"Go to the Brother at the entrance. He will give thee the black robe of service. Then repair to the kitchen and bring a tray of broth cups. Not yet have these poor ones been fed."

For the next three days Neri worked without cease. He helped to carry in newly stricken sufferers and to bear out the dead. He took food to houses where there was no one to cook and serve and with his own hands buried corpses fallen along the way-side. Now and then he caught a glimpse of Francesco Malavolti or joined him in some grim duty. Pale, unshaven, that gentleman looked a strange edition of his elegant self, but his blue eyes shone with ardour. He had sent his wife and children to the mountains but from the very first had himself remained at work. He told Neri that the shy young Simone da Cortone had been working like ten men and scarcely slept one hour uninterrupted. So many monks and priests had fled to safety that those who stayed were wanted day and night.

One morning as Neri hurried through the hospital corridor he saw something that brought his heart to his lips. It was a small figure in white framed in a black cloak. Standing in earnest converse with Matteo Cenni and a Dominican priest, composed as if she had never been away and had not returned to a welter of horror, was Catherine Benincasa.

With one wild impulse of joy Neri flung himself upon his knees before her. "*Mamma mia!* Dearest little Mamma, have you truly returned to your children? Blessed be God and all his Saints!"

"My beloved son!"

Her light firm hand rested on his head. Her tender smile bent upon his face. Only for an instant.

Then with a gesture which brought him to his feet, she presented him to the Dominican beside her. He was the new lector of the Order at Siena and Catherine's appointed confessor, Raimondo delle Vigne. Neri had an impression of aristocratic dignity and an analytical eye. The wonder flashed over him as to whether this man would appreciate the marvellous character of the woman he was appointed to guide. Then he turned to feast his tired eyes again on Catherine. But she was no longer beside him— gone, he knew, upon some errand of mercy. Neri's fleeting disappointment vanished immediately. She was here once more to be their fount of courage, the source of all their earthly happiness.

When Catherine Benincasa had time to think about the members of her circle during the next two months it was with divided feelings. On the one hand, she would fain have praised the courage with which they daily faced death from infection. She knew that with her it was different. She had attained a sense of oneness with the Spiritual World which obliterated those barriers between life and death felt so keenly by others. And yet to praise their efforts implied what she hoped with all her soul was never true—that these loyal men and women set her words higher than the blessed sense of serving God. It came to her clearly sometimes when she walked through the town in the laden silence of fetid nights that personality was at once a power for good and evil. Let hers become too dear to her companions and she would do them harm.

Yet how she loved them each and all. How torn her heart was by their sorrows and dangers.

Cecca Gori lost her three fine young sons; Lisa, her husband. Lapa was distracted with grief as one by one her beloved grandchildren were stricken with the dread disease. Into her great heart Catherine gathered them all, laboured to give them what was so clear to her—knowledge that real life was deathless and true love without separation. Yet were it not for midnight hours spent intensively in meditation, she could hardly have preserved her own sense of serene knowledge. Pain was too oppressive. She went from house to house where children had been left alone and the pathos of their fears, their suffering, their mortal cries left her spent with anguish.

Father Raimondo laboured with a calm valour which touched her deeply. For her keen perception told her he was no stoic. She was the more surprised one morning to meet him hurrying from the Mercy Hospital with such a look of despair that she stopped him swiftly.

"Father, what has happened now?"

"The Rector!" he panted. "Matteo Cenni has the dread disease. I go in haste to La Scala to procure medicines. But you know there is little help for the plague. So few recover. *Oimè!*" Tears started from his eyes. "That he—so needed, so skilled—should be taken from us!" He shook his head and hastened on.

Slowly, with bent head Catherine walked to the hospital. Many called out her name as she passed, but she did not hear. She was lost in an intense effort

of concentration. Brushing past the sobbing Brothers
in the corridor, paying no heed to Neri who stepped
forward to warn her, she went at once to the rector's
cell-like room. At the door she paused a moment.
Neri who had followed saw her face grow luminous
with joy. To his unbelieving ears he heard her call
out in a gay voice as she entered, "Come, come,
Matteo, rise at once! This is no time for thee to rest
in bed!"

Gliding swiftly to the couch where the man,
feverish and incapable of speech, had sunk down in
mortal illness, Catherine took his hands. Dazedly he
staggered to his feet. His glazed eyes fixed upon her
face. Dully he obeyed the pull of her arms and took
one step, then another. He tossed back his head, in-
haled a deep breath and smiled. "The illness leaves
me," he murmured. He withdrew from her support
and walked firmly to the door. "It is gone!" he
cried jubilantly.

Amazed faces, voices praising God, eyes stream-
ing with tears of gratitude, greeted those two as
they came down the stairs. But already they were
deep in talk about ways and means to get money to
feed the hungry. And when Father Raimondo
mournfully returned with his medicines he found
the rector sitting at his breakfast, eating raw onions.
Speechless the Dominican stared. It could not be!
His logical mind told him he was dreaming. But
Matteo's hearty laugh was not to be gainsaid.

Nor, indeed, could delle Vigne deny his own experience of healing. One breathless night in August
he rose for Office only to fall back with the violent

pains he had seen a hundred others suffer. At dawn
he was half carried by a friar to Catherine's house.
But already she was gone. He sank down prostrate
on a bench and prayed he might not die until she
came. Presently he was aware that she knelt beside
him. He felt her cool hand on his head. An inef-
fable freshness came from her presence to fill his
tortured senses with peace. For half an hour she
remained thus, then turned away and knelt before
the Crucifix. A trembling smote him and he knew
the end had come. In despair he saw her leave the
room without a glance his way.

Later Fra Raimondo heard her voice saying,
"*Ecco, il mio padre*, take this good nourishment."
He thought her strangely cruel to be so uncon-
cerned. But he took the hot soup and ate the bread
she brought. Shortly afterwards he fell asleep.
When he awoke he was himself again. Pain and
weakness had completely vanished. There in the little room where Catherine had spent so many hours
of passionate prayer he sat and marvelled at the
mystery of his recovery.

When this conscientious scholar first saw the circle gather at Catherine's house he thought he had
never seen such fusion of strange elements. It was
the last of August. Not once in all these weeks had
the members had time for more than a passing word
with one another. But now the worst of the plague
was at an end. The dead were buried, the hospitals
almost empty, the hungry provided for. And because of all the sorrow they had shared, the perils
endured and the terrific labour accomplished they

AS THEY DESCENDED, CATHERINE TURNED AGAIN AND AGAIN TO GLANCE BACK
AT SIENA

greeted each other with a thankfulness and joy which bade fair to swamp them in emotion.

Catherine, however, swept the group swiftly into that thought current which had been but deflected by immediate duties. How were they best to help with Gregory Eleventh's vast plan for the Crusade?

"*Ecco*, Neri and I shall set down the *brocca* and the basin to pick up the pen once more!" laughed Francesco Malavolti. "Is it not true, little Mamma? We shall stir the great lords to action."

"We must go and arouse the Bachelor from his solitude," urged Father Tantucci.

"We should take pilgrimages to religious houses nearby," said delle Vigne, "and awaken the zeal of their leaders."

To all of these ideas Catherine agreed. And so it was that when autumnal coolness slipped down into the valleys she set out with her confessor, Alessa and another Mantellata to visit the great convent of Santa Agnese at Montepulciano.

As they descended from the Porta Tufi, Catherine turned again and again to glance back at Siena. Girt with walls, it stood on a plateau above the valley. More than fifty tall towers of stone bristled upwards from all parts of the town. Their implication of war-like defence for ever smote her heart where the longing for peace was a constant ache. Gladly her eyes travelled to the dome and the square spired campanile of the cathedral. The shimmer of its rosy white and black marble in the early light renewed her faith in the true aspirations of her beloved city. From it she perceived flung out in the crystal air a thousand invisible lines which would some day bind Siena to the other Republics in a union of spirit. *Italia!* How few minds harboured the dimmest conception of a country, a nation.

Abruptly she turned and said to Fra Raimondo, "The Holy Father must return to Rome! Only so will hearts unite in this land."

The good man looked startled by her vehemence. His eyes had been idly following the course of a hare along the side of the road. "Daughter," he said, half in protest, half in admiration, "thou art ever at work. Thy mind rests not by day or night."

A teasing light shot into Catherine's eyes and then vanished as she said quickly with almost prophetic emphasis, "I have only this little point of present time and no more."

Between Siena and Montepulciano lies a curiously formed section of Tuscany. Hummock-like small hills with deeply scored pits between them intervene between higher ridges and all are enclosed within a rim of grape-coloured low mountains encircling the horizon. In those days thick forests between occasional small cleared farms were cut by unfertile desert stretches of powdery buff soil. The wild and lonely beauty of the landscape was heightened for the travellers by the sight of dark castles perched on hilltops. In these the great freebooting lords, like Cione Salimbeni, who gave no man or state allegiance, defied the world. Catherine liked better the small villages, walled about and brown as autumn leaves which nestled for safety on the crests of hills.

Up and down went the road. Often the party dismounted to rest their mules and plodded on for miles, singing as they went. Toward evening they made out Montepulciano. The town on its lofty height approached by long lines of cypress trees seemed to float toward them above the mist-filled valley. At its very edge was the great convent where Father Raimondo had been director so long. It was dedicated to the young and lovely Santa Agnese whose body lay within the chapel.

At Montepulciano and at nearby monasteries Catherine exerted a profound influence upon all with whom she came in contact and interest in the Crusade sprang up behind her footsteps. Moreover, the expedition gave to her confessor an excellent chance to know her better. By her inspired conversations with him, by her inexplicable knowledge of what was in his mind, by the effect she had upon him and upon everyone else of drawing life up to a higher plane of thought and action, she overcame every lingering doubt he had as to her true spiritual significance. There was no precedent for such a woman. Everything about her was phenomenal. The ecclesiastical world hardly provided for her possible activity. But Raimondo made up his mind that she had a mission, a mission of tremendous import to the Church and that he, knowing her to be divinely guided, would lend all his powerful influence to assure her freedom of action.

On their return to Siena, delle Vigne found his resolution supported by the loftiest authority. Awaiting Catherine was a most distinguished churchman. Alfonso di Vadaterra, a Spaniard was he. Once a Bishop, he had abandoned his high place to set an example of unworldliness to others and had been appointed confessor and travelling companion for the noble and powerful Princess Bridget of Sweden. This woman, highly endowed and passionately devoted to the cause of Christendom, had laboured for years to influence the Pope to return to Rome. She travelled all about Italy with her children and her suite, preaching and endeavouring to sway those in places of power. Later she was canonized as Saint Bridget.

It was now only a year or two after her death when her confessor presented himself before Catherine Benincasa. No greater contrast could have been imagined than that existing between the wealthy Swedish seer with her brilliant train and the little Mantellata in her simple home in Fontebranda. To the enlightened eye of Vadaterra, however, appeared only what the two women had in common— a spiritual ideal. Reverently he greeted Catherine and told her he had come to her directly from Pope Gregory. His Holiness had sent to her a special indulgence and a special request—that she should aid by her prayers the organization of the Crusade.

Catherine's joy was unbounded. As for Father Raimondo, he immediately felt justified in urging her to accept an invitation to go to Pisa. Both the Holy Cross and the Misericordia convents had repeatedly begged her presence there. She reflected deeply. But in the end it seemed an opportunity to fulfil the Pope's request. Pisa on the sea which seemed so close to the East—there she could preach the Crusade! Late in January, 1375, with three of the Mantellate, she set out.

After that last terrible defeat at the hands of Genoa the proud maritime Republic of Pisa was like a ghost city. Just enough shipping remained to keep it alive and give the visitor a sense of its vivid past. There were still dromedaries in the streets along the wharves and merchants still displayed silks and filigree work, spices and dried fruits from Oriental markets. But the old bustling aggressive roar of trade and battle had sunk to a whisper. It was a city where scholarship flourished and men's minds, defeated by earthly struggle, turned heavenward. That piazza terminating one corner of the city where the Cathedral, the Baptistry, the Leaning Tower and the Campo Santo form one of the most marvellous structural groups in Europe, seemed in its white peace and isolation to typify the very spirit of Pisa.

Catherine, Alessa and their two companions were received by a noble Pisan family, the Buonconti, and entertained in their palace. It was situated just back from the Arno, the turgid river which sweeps through the city directly into the sea. This was a rich section of the town and what mercantile activity there was took place up and down the street. No locality, therefore, could have been more favourable for the crowds that came seeking this famous visitor. They besieged the Buonconti house and followed her about the streets. To touch her garments, to press her fingers to their lips, to hear her speak a single word brought to the faces of these men and women a look of rapture.

Mediæval worship of holiness, beside which royalty and riches were as nothing, lingered in this dream-like city. The coming of Catherine caused something very like a modern revival. People in such numbers repented their sins and asked for confessors and priests that Father delle Vigne and Fra Bartolommeo had to be sent for in haste. Wherever Catherine went—to the two convents, to the island monastery by boat where she preached to the Brothers, to the cathedral, to the monastery at the beautiful Campo Santo—there went crowds to follow her with fervent interest.

This interest was reciprocated. She never wearied of looking into the faces which revealed so much, or of hearing the human problems which evoked her compassion. When Father delle Vigne asked her reproachfully why she permitted people to kiss her hand, she looked at him with startled eyes. "I did not think about that," she said. "I was heeding only the persons themselves."

Naturally the sensation she created provoked criticism. It was a great shock to the intellectuals that this untutored maid from afar should stir the city so profoundly. The matter was taken in hand one day by a learned churchman and his associate, Count Pietro degli Albizzi, a doctor of laws. Admitted to the Buonconti palace, they demanded an opportunity of questioning Catherine. Father Bartolommeo who summoned her then saw re-enacted the scene with the two Augustinians at Fonte

Branda. "Must God not have had a mouth and tongue to create the world by speech?" Such were the clap-trap questions.

Catherine had come into the presence of her visitors straight from a long period of meditation and the light of that translating experience was beautiful upon her face. With simple earnestness she brushed aside their profitless interrogations.

"What is necessary to you and to me is to know that our Lord has reclothed our whole nature in order to save us, that He suffered and died to buy us back. Yes, what is necessary to me is to believe it and to meditate upon it until my heart is inflamed with love for Him who has loved so much."

Such eloquence of adoration sounded in these words that Albizzi fell upon his knees before her. Something he had never known before had been conveyed straight to his heart. Before he left, as a supreme mark of personal esteem, he begged Catherine to present his baby son for baptism and when she promised to do so he went away with a face brimming over with elation.

During this interview there had entered the room a man whom Catherine had seen often during her stay—one whose heartfelt encomiums had first aroused the interest of the city in having her come. It was that same Father Lazzarino who had left the Sienese University to become a hermit in Pisa. For him to listen to this interrogation meant all the bitterness of reliving his own hateful conduct toward the Mantellata when he was at the University. The moment the two visitors were gone, as if he felt to blame for their advent, he apologized to Catherine and cried out bitterly, "O cursed intellectualism! Dryer than dust without the tears of humility!"

"Truly, so it is," she replied quietly and smiled. But she had had enough personal emotion for one session. What she wanted was action and immediately she sought out Alessa to ask her to write a letter. In her eagerness to respond to Pope Gregory's need, Catherine was sending off communications every day to the far corners of Italy. Now she dictated a second letter to the great Queen Giovanna of Naples.

Something about that woman had caught Catherine's imagination. She felt in her a force which might be turned to good instead of evil. And, indeed, this royal personality was highly endowed in every way but one. She was one of the foremost beauties of Italy. She was astute, rich, powerful and magnetic. What she lacked was a shred of conscience—let alone any aspiration toward virtue. She had been deeply implicated in the murder of her first husband. Her luxurious and licentious court was the scandal of Europe. When the Swedish princess Bridget visited Naples with her daughter Karin and her son Karlo the unscrupulous queen deliberately entered into a love intrigue with the attractive boy. Dazzled and hypnotized by this charmer twice his age, so casually married for the third time, the young Prince flung to the winds all respect for his noble-minded mother and would have entered upon the fatal alliance had not his sudden death prevented.

All this was known to Catherine Benincasa. But she approached Queen Giovanna with the hope that there might be some crack in her worldly enamel into which the right word might penetrate and so change the selfish heart beneath. It was for aggressive egoists such as she that the Crusade might prove the one way toward goodness. And it seemed for a moment as if that crack had actually been discovered. For the siren of Naples sent the young Dominican a gracious reply promising to help.

As a matter of fact, those letters of Catherine's had proved quite a sensation in Naples. Wherever, indeed, those fiery communications went they made an enormous impression. This was partly due to the intensity of spirit injected into every line, partly to the beauty and force of Catherine's phrasing and partly to the simple fact that she wrote in her native tongue. Remember that most communications were composed in Latin. Remember, also, that up to this time practically nothing had been written in Italian except poetry. It is no wonder, therefore, that these documents were received with excitement, read with attention and cherished with a reverent care which has preserved them through the centuries. They represent the first great Italian prose writing.

June brought to Catherine and her friends in Pisa news which at first appeared encouraging. Bernabo Visconti of Milan had signed an armistice with the Cardinal at Bologna. But delle Vigne pointed out that an immense fly floated in this ointment.

"Do not forget," said he to the assembled group, "who has been fighting for the Cardinal against Bernabo. Remember that now that fierce captain and his hired soldiers will be free for more devil's work. Where next will Giovanni Acuto stir up war and trouble?"

Giovanni Acuto was the name Italians gave to the notorious English freebooting warrior, John Hawkwood. He lived by selling his services at arms and by terrorizing the countryside, and delle Vigne's question was all too soon answered. Released by the Cardinal who had hired him, the desperado with his troops now swept down upon the greatest of Tuscan cities.

Florence, lately afflicted by the plague followed by famine, was in no position to fight this band of cut-throats. In desperation the city sent for aid to the Papal Legate. But he haughtily returned the reply that he could do nothing unless he was sent 60,000 gold florins. Moreover, despite the fact that he had received orders from the Pope to send relief, the Legate forbade any grain to be forwarded to the starving city. This action produced in Florence an outburst of patriotic fury. Determining not to submit to the vengeful Cardinal, the Republic preferred the greater expense of buying off Hawkwood. And this they did. They sent the bandit warrior away with bursting pockets to continue elsewhere his career of thieving.

Catherine had just dismissed a visitor one evening and was about to seek the family in the cool, high-ceilinged dining-room where they sat at supper when Tommaso Buonconti burst through the outer door. His face was black as thunder and with a gesture almost wild he beckoned her to come with him to join the others.

"Terrible news!" he shouted. So startling was this apparition that everyone at the table was arrested in the very act of eating. Alessa choked on her fig pastry and Francesco Buonconti looked up at his brother with jaws dripping with the juice of a veal chop he was gnawing.

"That demon in human form, Giovanni Acuto, is camped outside of Pisa!" went on Tommaso. "He has sent messengers to the Government that he will kindly spare the city destruction if we will pay him ninety thousand gold florins!"

Francesco stopped to wipe his mouth and then cried angrily, "But we can raise no such sum! Pisa is poor."

"Still less can Pisa raise an army to fight this robber," declared Father Lazzarino reasonably.

"It is so," agreed Tommaso. "We shall attempt to make Acuto take less money to be gone. But the governors will proceed with caution. *Piano, piano!* Let us hope we anger him not or he will slay and burn without mercy."

Catherine had been standing at the door. Gently she said: "Let us hope for the best. Meanwhile I shall write this Acuto a letter."

Two days later she handed to delle Vigne a parchment addressed to the English captain. She began the missive as she began her letters to friends, to the Pope, to everyone. It was a formula satisfying to her humility. "I, Caterina, servant and slave of the servants of Jesus Christ write in His precious Blood, with desire to see you ——" In this case it was "a true son and knight of Christ."

I beg you gently in Christ Jesus [went on the message] that since God and also our Holy Father have ordered a Crusade against the infidels and you take such pleasure in war and fighting, you should not make war against Christians any more—for this is a wrong to God, but go against the infidels!

When he had read this plea, Catherine's confessor shook his head. "My daughter, that heart is too black for word of yours to touch."

Yet he took the parchment and with another Dominican rode out to the mercenaries' camp to present it in person to the commander. Led before the great mailed figure, the priest addressed him in fear and trembling and waited anxiously for the terse villain to finish reading. To his utter astonishment the Englishman shouted for his chiefs and not only swore himself, but made the others swear on the Sacrament, that they would do as the Sienese maid requested and would go and fight with the Crusaders against the Turks.

Delle Vigne's report of this encounter fairly rocked the Buonconti palace and impressed the brothers more than the fact that Hawkwood had accepted Pisan terms and was about to leave the city in peace. Catherine, however, was not surprised. In that other world where she lived in contemplation she knew marvels beside which every human event was inconsiderable. More than ever she gave herself to that inner life these days, for what with the unrest seething throughout Italy and the responsibilities heaped upon her, she had to keep clear her sense of infinite perspective.

Right across the street from the Buonconti palace, almost on the bank of the river, was the small church of Santa Cristina. There Catherine spent hours absorbed in prayer. One day before that altar she was vouchsafed an experience of which but one other human instance had ever been recorded.

Father Raimondo and Alessa, who had accompanied her to the service, knelt some distance away. Suddenly they saw her sink to the pavement. Her out-stretched, rigid arms, the agony and bliss upon her face told them instantly this was no usual form of ecstasy. Bending over her, they found she could neither move nor speak and suffered frightfully. Together they carried her back to her room and hung over her for days. All they could do to alleviate her exhaustion from continual pain was to bathe her hands, which seemed to hurt her most, with a special wine provided by a friend. More than once they thought she was dying and their anxiety spread about the town until the house was besieged with solicitous visitors.

"What is it? What has happened? Why is she so ill?" All day long the Mantellate and Fra Raimondo heard these questions.

They replied with hesitation. To explain was difficult, was even dangerous—so little was such a thing likely to be understood. True, Saint Francis of Assisi had had this same marvellous experience, but that had happened over a hundred years ago and had long been accepted. Even those who loved Catherine and believed in her more than in anyone on earth made no attempt to follow the mystery of this complete penetration into the event of Golgotha. They only knew that so absolutely had she imagined the sacrifice of Christ that there in the church she had felt physically the wounds inflicted on the Cross. She had received the Stigmata. Until the end of her life she was conscious of recurrent pain which to her was a blissful sign of oneness with the Son of God.

There is not the slightest doubt that this manifestation increased Catherine's power. A man who afterwards became a famous leader in the Church declared that his contact with her in Pisa was one of the great events of his life and that he was dumbfounded to find her words "so profound, fiery and powerful." Indeed, work for individuals was always richly rewarding to her. What proved baffling was the task of dealing with the battling forces of Italy.

Events of late July decided the peacemaker to return home. On the twenty-fourth of that month Milan and Florence agreed upon a five-year pact to oppose the Church and at once set out ambassadors to win over to their side every other important city north of Rome. In order to do what she could to hold Siena firm against this League, Catherine spent August there. She summoned courage to tell everyone that work for the Crusade must be laid aside for the mitigation of local evils. She visited the

Bachelor of Lecceto, comforted her mother, held daily meetings with her circle of friends. But in September an urgent request from Gregory Eleventh sent her back again for the Mediterranean shore—this time to steady Lucca against the wiles of Florence.

Neri di Landoccio joined the travellers on this occasion and found every step of the long journey fraught with interest. As they approached the sea his eyes roamed with delight from the plain to its ring of jagged mountains, from the dusty white road, edged with palm trees and pomegranates, to the castles perched on crags. At last stern walls suddenly rose up to cut the city of Lucca from its flat surroundings—walls so thick and wide that a road bordered with trees ran about the top and Neri could see horsemen galloping at full speed high above the ground.

After they had settled down in their lodgings near the Dominican church of San Romano, the young man strolled about the town. He was entranced with the Duomo, the delicate façade of which consists of tiers of slender pillars, and had the good luck to see it adorned and lighted from one end to the other during the city's greatest religious festival. This Exaltation of the Holy Cross brought the entire population to see the adored relic and participate in a magnificent processional. Much of the fervour thus aroused was concentrated on the celebrated Mantellata from Siena and crowds followed her about the streets.

Catherine spent a large proportion of each day in

conferences with dignitaries both of the Church and of the Republic and she laboured to persuade them to obey the Pope. Yet in the great cause she never forgot individual needs. One morning in the midst of dictating to Neri an important letter, she suddenly broke off. Looking at him anxiously, she said, "My son, thy soul is heavy. What weighs upon it?"

With a deep sigh the secretary confessed that he was once more in the grip of confusion and self-doubt. Gently she consoled him and said with her prophetic look that she was certain he would find his ultimate goal and his soul's salvation. For the fathomless comfort of this assurance Neri evermore held dear the memory of Lucca.

After a brief sojourn in the town Catherine and her companions went on to Pisa. There her work for the cause of Gregory held such promise of success that the Archbishop sent a special request to the Dominican Provincial to have her remain longer. Her luminous faith shone like a star against these gathering clouds of disaffection. Then word came that Siena itself had enrolled under that red banner inscribed with *Libertas* which the League had unfurled. This happened on November twenty-seventh and within ten days five other towns rose against the Papal Legates.

It was Fra Raimondo who brought the last of these grim tidings. With another Brother he hurried to the hospital near the Dominican church where Catherine was staying. Bursting in upon her as she was dictating to Neri, he cried out, "Perugia is lost! Perugia is one of the five cities to join the League!"

Sinking down upon the window-seat and covering his face with his hands, this man of iron self-possession broke into despairing tears. Neri had leaped up and was pacing the room in great agitation. But to the amazement of the others, Catherine sat still with no sign of emotion. She seemed withdrawn, almost impassive.

Finally she said slowly, "Milk and honey is this compared to what will follow." Coolly she met the incredulous eyes turned upon her and added, "The clergy will divide among themselves before this struggle ends."

Without illusion, with unearthly foresight, she realized exactly what was coming. She had no valid hope of stemming the tide of distrust, hatred and will to victory that was washing over both Church and people. Yet without hesitation she laboured to bring peace between the contestants. In this selfless readiness to associate herself with failure and the lost cause of love, she revealed a greatness of spirit never surpassed by mortal.

It was nearly Christmas when Catherine and the others again reached Siena. Snowflakes were in the air. Every church and chapel had its little crèche with the painted wooden figures of shepherds adoring the Bambino and the Virgin. The great cantatas soared above the prostrate multitudes. And among them, kneeling on the stone floor beside her mother, lifting a rapt and joyous face, was Monna Lapa's

daughter. She forgot all else that day in her gratitude for Love made manifest on earth.

No one in that age, however, was long permitted
to forget that he who loves must battle. Hardly had
1376 begun when from Avignon came tidings of a
character to arouse every drop of Catherine's fighting blood. Two issues were at stake—the Pope's
failure to support those few cities remaining loyal
to him and his greater mistake of further irritating
his Italian subjects by the type of churchmen he
selected in creating nine new Cardinals. Not only
were seven of them French, but among those was
the unscrupulous and hated Gérard du Puy, the
Abbot of Marmoutier in Perugia. In a passion of
protest Catherine dictated a letter to the Pope re-
pudiating his unwisdom. That letter became
famous. And no wonder! When one remembers that
this self-educated child of the people was addressing the highest single authority in the Western
world the tone of the message is simply astounding.

I have been to Pisa and Lucca, until now urging them
as much as I could not to join the League with rotten
members who rebel against you. But they are greatly per-
plexed because they have no encouragement from you and
are being continually urged and threatened from the
other side to join it. But up to the present they have not
quite given in. . . .

I have heard that you have created Cardinals. I believe
it would be more to the honour of God and better for
yourself if you would always take care to choose virtuous
men. When the contrary is done it is a great insult to
God and disaster to the Holy Church. We must not be
surprised afterwards if God sends us His chastisements

and scourges, for it is but just. I beseech you do what you have to do manfully and with the fear of God. . . .

Even to set down such words left Francesco Malavolti weak and breathless. When the letter had been dispatched by special messenger he sought out Neri and took him for a ramble to vent in exercise his pent-up feelings of awe and amazement. Out through the Porta Pispini they went and southward through the strange country—partly desert, partly forest and partly farmland. From every rise of ground they could see the lofty outline of Monte Amiata and at every step they thought of that spiritual height on which stood the woman they had the privilege of serving.

When they returned at the hour of repast the young men found Catherine talking with Ser Cristofano di Gano Guidini. In his extravagant fashion he was saying, "Dearest Mamma, again I would thank thee for thy precious letter which I shall keep until the day of my death because thou didst write it and because, even at a time when thou wert labouring for the Holy Father, thou didst not forget me, most unworthy of thy sons."

Neri and Francesco exchanged a look. That such was the inclusive character of their leader's great affections had been the subject of their discourse all afternoon.

Catherine laughed gaily at this encomium. "Thou didst put to me a difficult problem in thy letter," she said to the notary. "It is hardly within my province to advise upon a plan of matrimony. Since that time

I have heard only that thou hast taken a wife. Tell me, didst thou choose the lady I advised or another?"

Cristofano looked very foolish. "Another," he murmured confusedly. Then, as the others grew mirthful over this confession, he added earnestly, "But she is good and excellent as a wife, is my Mattia, daughter of Fede di Turino, the furrier of Provenzano. She is excellent as a wife!"

Catherine regarded him with teasing eyes. "I knew thou wouldst not accept my choice. But it is well. I hoped only to clarify thy mind on the subject."

As she turned away to greet Father Tantucci just arrived from Lecceto, Francesco Malavolti whispered to Neri, "Is it not as I said? She knows all we think. Once when I tried to deny a fault I had committed she cried out, 'Thou canst do nothing or say nothing that I do not know.' I believe her, truly. She knows well it is hard for me to be good."

Neri listened and smiled. But his thoughts were on vaster matters. He had learned much since being in Pisa all those months. "She is the one, the only one," he said gravely, "who can do aught in these troublous times. I feel, Francesco, that this is a year wherein great changes will be wrought. And through her! There is no one like her."

The young man was a true prophet. The year 1376 was perhaps the most momentous year of Catherine Benincasa's life.

Chapter Six

"ALESSA, wilt thou inquire who among the Fellowship sup with us tonight?"

In the dim hall of Santa Maria della Scala Hospital Catherine Benincasa turned a smile upon her friend. Then she added, "I myself must go into the hall of the sick for a time. There lie two grievously wounded in one of these family quarrels which plague Siena."

"I doubt not all will come to the supper," murmured Alessa.

Catherine laughed gaily. "*Buona!* There is bread enough, at least. I myself this morning baked nine loaves and Sano di Maco has sent the wine. Lisa will help thee with the rest."

As the speaker's quick step carried her into the hospital room, Alessa turned to await the others. Slowly they were coming up the stairs from the

Church of the Madonna under the vault of the hospital. Nearly twenty of the circle had assembled there this late afternoon of January, 1376. Before their leader had begun her journeys the members used to hold these convocations often. And now that she was back they had requested her to meet with them again to give them rules of life for a difficult period, to rekindle their faith and share with them her knowledge.

With the most passionate attention the group had listened to her words. She seemed to touch the peculiar need of each one in turn. Cristofano di Gano, the notary, was struck by her saying, "He who in administering justice tries to please others or fears to displease, so as not to injure himself, is a slave." Francesco Malavolti treasured the phrase, "We must rise above ourselves." Neri's heart expanded to the assurance, "He who conforms to the Will of God finds peace."

In that glorious sense of oneness and affection always induced by such a focussing of mutual aspiration, all were laughing and teasing one another as they entered the great hall. And there Alessa took the roll call for the subsequent reunion. It appeared that everyone, but two, was coming. Matteo Cenni had to be back at the Misericordia and Fra Bartolommeo had been called to the sick-bed of a parishioner.

"But Sano di Maco will be there," said Andrea Vanni. "He told me so today when I stepped into his place of business. Poor mother Alessa—so many hungry mouths to feed!"

"Have no fear, my son," cried Monna Lapa with a comfortable laugh, "already the pot of soup simmers with leeks for the *cenacolo*."

Neri, Francesco, and Giovanni Tolomei passed out together into the grave and quiet square. As they started across toward the cathedral, Vanni came up behind them and took them by the arms. "Stop and look at the white campanile in the sunset light," said he. "Is it not like our Mamma, so joyous, yet reaching ever upwards to Heaven?"

Near the palace of the Captain of the People a group of urchins were giving a miniature representation of the great game *pugna*. For an instant they desisted to stare at the young men. Then with evident recognition, they sung out with one united howl of derision, "Caterinati! Caterinati!"

Francesco laughed. "Those ugly little ones shout that name in scorn for our devotion to the little Mamma, but how sweetly it rings in our ears."

Vanni, on the contrary, had looked back, frowning. "But they repeat in that fashion the evil wag of tongues in Siena. No one will believe a woman so surrounded by men of every sort, a woman who travels about the country and is visited by the high and great, could be and is holy as the blessed water in the cathedral basin. I hear it everywhere—this wicked gossip."

Young Tolomei, of angelic face, said quietly, "To love so deeply, to love so many as doth our sweetest Mamma is, truly, to run dangers. Not alone spring they from the stupid world, but from ourselves. Like Monna Lapa we wish her beside us always and that is wrong."

For an instant all four were silent. They had reached the sublime, unfinished arch spanning the street to the right—all that existed or ever would exist of that dreamed immensity in marble, the new cathedral. Under its delicate curve they observed two horsemen pacing slowly away toward the main street and talking earnestly together.

"There goes young Stefano Maconi!" murmured Neri. "Who rides beside him?"

"What? Thou knowest him not?" cried Francesco and Andrea in one breath.

Vanni struck a swaggering pose in imitation of the man in question. "The very learned scholar and skilled in science; the notable ambassador to Perugia and elsewhere; the plotter against the government, so heavily fined some five years gone by; the man courted by many and feared by more; the lusty hater; the doughty fighter ——"

"Enough!" interrupted Neri laughing. "Thou wouldst name Nanni di Vanni Savini."

"The same," assented Francesco, "called Nanni di Ser Vanni, who has himself summoned as peacemaker only that he may stir up further trouble between families."

As they descended the long, steep stairs beside the cathedral to the Baptistery, Giovanni Tolomei said with seraphic slyness, "I hear the Bachelor of Lecceto hath tried to lure this Ser Vanni into better ways. He tells him to visit our Mamma."

"*Benissimo!*" cried Francesco with a grin,

"should he do that, his fate is certain. No more fighting or double-dealing for him! Oh, that I might see that meeting! The bold scapegrace will find his match."

At the foot of the stairs the four parted until the hour of the *cenacolo*. Francesco would hasten home to his wife; Vanni, to see a member of the Signoria; Tolomei, for an hour of prayer at San Domenico. As for Neri, he had to dispatch a letter dictated by Catherine just before they both left for the Church of the Madonna.

As he dipped down into the via Fonte Branda, the secretary reflected deeply upon that letter and upon the writer of it. Only that morning the heart-breaking news had come that Pisa and Lucca had joined the Florentine League against the Papal Legates. The ring of enemies against the Church was now solid and complete—for all Catherine's effort to hold those cities firm! He himself could see no outlet for the situation and felt profound despair. But—she! She had only winced at the blow. Already she was writing her combination of comfort and protest to the rebellious cities. And her face as she talked in the chapel that afternoon had worn a holy calm which gave no hint of pain and bitter disappointment. Did she hope the Holy Father could still make peace?

If so, it looked a few days later as if that hope were not unfounded. Joyful news was brought to Fonte Branda on the eighth day after the New Year —this time by an unwonted messenger, Sano di Maco, the merchant and banker. That individual, a friend of the Benincasas even before the day of Catherine's prominence, had not only joined her circle, but acted as its financial manager, arranging journeys and affairs. Everyone held this man of substance in respectful affection.

Now as he stood in the hallway, with his knee-length, fur-trimmed mantle and bronze pen-case hanging at his belt, he was the very picture of bourgeois stability. Alessa took one look at his expression and followed him up the stairs. Catherine was dictating two letters at once to Neri and Francesco. But as the visitor entered the room all three sprang to their feet.

Gravely the merchant spoke. "To the Republic has come a message of good cheer—a circular letter issued by His Holiness. Il Papa announces his intention of returning to Rome—there to establish his Holy See."

After the first outburst of rejoicing had subsided Catherine sent Francesco to fetch Father Raimondo from Camporeggi. When he had come and heard the message, she said to him quietly: "It is one thing to announce the departure and another thing to go. Think you not so, Father?"

The Dominican had assumed his most analytical expression. "Even the intention is excellent," said he slowly. "But what will influence the League still more is an overture of peace from His Holiness." Upon this he exchanged a long, silent regard with Catherine. Then with a sigh, he added, "Before too much lightness of heart, let us wait to hear his message to the Florentines."

They did not have long to wait. A month after he had issued that general letter Gregory sent to Florence a terrible indictment and demanded that the ringleaders of the revolt be sent to him by the thirty-first of March. Catherine learned this with peculiar anguish. For among those ringleaders was a man she had met in Florence—a man who had been kindness itself, not alone to her, but to her brothers. He was the rich and prominent merchant, Niccolò Soderini, who during the last two months had been a member of the Florentine government.

In a very passion of suffering love she sent word to each of the antagonists. To the Pope she wrote in behalf of the rebellious Republic.

I beseech you on the part of Christ Crucified to show me this mercy. Overcome their malice by your kindness. We are yours, O Father. . . . Even if there is no excuse for wrong-doing, nevertheless, on account of the wrongs, injustices and iniquities they had to endure from bad pastors and rulers, it seemed to them they could not do otherwise. . . . Therefore, Father, I implore mercy for them. I tell you, sweet Christ on earth, on the part of Christ in heaven, that if you act thus, without quarrel or tempest, they will all come and put their heads in your lap, with sorrow for their offences. . . . Peace, Peace, Peace! So that war may not delay this sweet time.

To Niccolò Soderini she dictated an impassioned plea for reconciliation with Gregory.

The moment has come to weep and lament for the Bride of Christ is persecuted by perfidious and corrupt members. This is why I beg you, my sons and daughters, to pour out before God fervent prayers and pious supplications for the Holy Church which is so violently persecuted. He who goes against the Church becomes his own enemy for She is no other than Christ Himself and gives us the sacraments which give life. . . . How stupid and absurd for the limbs to rebel against the head . . . especially when it is known that heaven and earth will pass before the head loses its power.

It was Catherine's conviction that two wrongs never made a right. Bearing arms against the French Legates would not assure success against oppression in her opinion. In the hope of securing the active influence of William Flete, she betook herself with friends one March day when willows were silver-green along the rivulet out to Lecceto and talked the matter over with the Bachelor.

He agreed with her ideas in every respect. What caused him to marvel was her willingness to remain in the midst of such a furious world. "To adore God in the peace of the wilderness is better," he protested.

Catherine rested her eyes upon this Augustinian with his Saxon colouring and handsome features, so different in cast from those of her race. Then she uttered an irrepressible laugh at his utter contentment with his chosen lot. Shaking her head, she replied, "But what of the people whose souls go astray in this conflict?"

As if her words reminded him of an important matter, his eyes lighted. "Thou, with thy hunger for souls, my daughter, mayst rejoice to receive a black—a very black sheep. Nanni di Ser Vanni hath promised me to visit thee soon."

From afar the Mantellata brought back her at-

tention to assure the hermit she would welcome his
protégé. Then she rose to go. It was a long walk
back to Siena and already it was far past noon. Neri,
delle Vigne, Lisa and Cristofano di Gano had returned from taking dinner at the convent and were
lingering outside the Bachelor's cave. He came forth
to bid them adieu. Finally, with a touching gesture
of reverence, he lifted the worn hem of Catherine's
black mantle and pressed it to his lips. Cristofano,
who frequently observed this action of William
Flete, made respectful note of it in his *Memoires.*

Not long after this excursion to Lecceto the
heralded black sheep kept his word. Nanni di Ser
Vanni knocked upon Catherine's door. With canny
duplicity, however, he deliberately chose for his
visit an hour which would coincide with the Mantellata's service at the Misericordia and only Fra
Raimondo was at the house to receive him.

Craftily delle Vigne kept the suave buccaneer
talking about himself till, at last, the door opened
and Catherine glided swiftly in. With a face of
eager welcome, she began speaking to her guest in
a fashion later described by her confessor as,
"wounding him with one hand while she doctored
him with the other." Her intelligent and persuasive
argument obviously charmed Ser Vanni's mind—
even as he winced at the thrust of her truths. But
he was conscious of a deeper and more unfamiliar
appeal than to the intellect.

When he finally rose to take his leave, it was
with a courtier's bow. "I would not be so ungra-
cious," said he to Catherine, "as to say no to every-

thing you ask of me. Four bitter enmities have I at this telling and for your sake I shall give up one of them."

Catherine said nothing. Her eloquent eyes rested upon him with the warm, caressing tolerance of a parent regarding a beloved and wayward child. Ser Vanni crossed the room and at the door bowed once more.

Then, as he lifted his head and met again that magnetic glance, he jerked upright. *"Dio mio!"* he exclaimed. "Never before have I felt anything like this. I cannot leave! I can refuse you nothing!"

Fra Raimondo, standing very still beside the oaken cupboard, watched the two faces—the alarmed resistance of the man, the tender assurance of the woman. Then he heard Ser Vanni say softly, with a sweeping gesture of surrender, "You have won!" The next instant he had cast himself at Catherine's feet, swearing he would turn his mind to goodness and imploring her blessing.

Gravely sweet, she gave it, turned him over to delle Vigne for confession and left the room. Outside she found Francesco Malavolti. Aware of whom she had been receiving, his blue eyes danced with mischief. But, though Catherine could not help smiling at him, she whisked him off at once to write a letter and gave him no chance for humour at the expense of Siena's darling villain.

That instance of personal force redirected through her toward good was some consolation for the terrible events which now followed one upon the other. The Papal armies had battle after battle with the forces of the League and the latter appeared to be winning. Messengers these days streamed in and out of the Quarter of the Goose. Father delle Vigne had joined his efforts to Catherine's and was writing constantly to Florence. He reminded the rebels that the Pope possessed the one single authority obeyed throughout Europe and that to tempt him to vengeance was madness. He begged them to have some peaceful measure to propose when they sent their representatives to Avignon in answer to Gregory's command.

Before the middle of March, Fra Raimondo received a reply from the party in power at Florence. At once he brought it to show Catherine. He had been asked in Catherine Benincasa's name to go to Avignon and pave the way for the Florentine envoys.

"In thy name, daughter, they ask this!" Delle Vigne looked at the face now so alight with hope and gladness. He reflected that he had made no mistake in recognizing her mission as of paramount significance. One year of activity had brought her name to the lips of every Italian who had any wish to check discord and bloodshed.

When Fra Raimondo received permission from the head of the Dominican Order to go to Avignon on this errand, the excitement of the Fellowship knew no bounds. Now, indeed, they were in the very thick of the vast struggle. With blessings and good wishes they sped him on his way together with the twenty others who joined him in the expedition. Delle Vigne bore with him Catherine's fourth letter to the Pope. In it she begged for three measures: clemency toward his erring subjects, reform within the Church, and his own return to Rome.

Confidence in delle Vigne's influence helped Catherine bear another sudden blow—the entrance of Bologna into the League. But there was worse to come. A huge body of Papal troops, commanded by John Hawkwood, attacked and captured the town of Faenza—south-east of Bologna. Without quarter the savage warriors annihilated the inhabitants. Brutally they slew men, women and children.

In her anguish over this spot of blood upon the escutcheon of the Church, Catherine found relief in bringing peace to one minute corner of Italy. A deputation of nobles visited her one day and asked her to serve as mediator in a savage and long-enduring quarrel between three Sienese families. Eagerly she promised to receive representatives from all the factions involved.

And thus it was that one afternoon a tall young man went swinging down the hill to Fonte Branda. He had not wished to come. He thought it was absurd for people of consequence to consult a youthful Mantellata—and a dyer's daughter, to boot! But since the Rinaldini and the Tolomei had already agreed to do so, he could not refuse. Besides, he could hardly deny his mother's tearful request that he visit this Catherine. Personally he was not much pleased to settle the quarrel. He loved the excitement of galloping through the streets and dealing a good sword thrust at his enemies. What was more worthy of a man than to fight for the honour of his

house? Thus mused Stefano Maconi as he walked
through the Contrada of the Goose.

Long afterwards young Maconi wrote of that
first encounter, with Catherine:

"She received me, not with the timid fear of a young
girl, as I had supposed, but with a tenderness of a young
girl who saw her brother after a long journey. I was
impressed and said, 'The finger of God is here.'"

Never did he realize, however, how accurately
this impression corresponded to fact. When Catherine first heard his name in connection with the quarrel she was to mediate, it was with a mere vague
twinge of memory. But the instant the tall young
nobleman stepped into her house, the twenty-three
years since she had seen him last rolled back like a
curtain. Once more she stood beside her father in
the court of the Maconi house and gazed longingly
after a laughing little boy in velvet doublet, wishing
she might give him a flower. As she greeted this
stalwart version of that charming child, it was with
no sense of his being a stranger and she knew that
destiny had not brought him again before her for a
casual reason.

Reading in his wide-apart eyes amazement at
finding her so different from the pious pedant he
had expected, she talked to him a little about the
things she had at heart. Surely a youth with so fine
a face would respond to a grander challenge than
that of merely defending by the sword the honour
of his house! The Crusade, Church reform, the return of the Pope to Rome, work for peace through-

out all Italy—such was the perspective she unrolled. As she did so her eyes glowed with enthusiasm and her voice rang with the authority of one experienced in great affairs.

Suddenly she rose from the wooden settle under the high window. "Friends come shortly for the *cenacolo* and I must cease this sweet converse. As to the settlement of the quarrel, leave these things to me." Her smile shone out upon him.

In reluctant silence Stefano Maconi stood before her. His handsome, boyish face revealed his thoughts to her as if it had been an open book. She saw that upon the vast horizon she had opened before him, the petty contentions of the local nobles had already dwindled to a mere speck. Already he was longing to serve, to be received into the magic circle of the Fellowship.

"May I return?" he stammered, "May I learn more, help you in some way?"

Gladly Catherine bade the young man come as often as he wished. She had a clear sense of his simple goodness, his fidelity and affectionate warmth which would fit him for a place in those mighty tasks confronting a distraught world. Stefano found a warm welcome awaiting him from Neri and Francesco and from the moment of his first entrance into the circle both he and all the others took it for granted he was an integral part of it. Once accepted as one of Catherine's sons, young Maconi flung away his sword forever and without regret and found it a more exciting task than any he had ever had to assist with her correspondence.

Even in these wild days she continued to write her friends in cities, monasteries and convents. But her chief concern, of course, was to communicate constantly with Fra Raimondo. With impatient anxiety she waited during those early days of April for his first letter. She wrote begging him to ask the Pope if he would not receive her, also, at Avignon. But when at last delle Vigne sent her details of the interview between Gregory and the Florentine hostages, she was thunderstruck.

In the first place, the Pope was displeased because, not the individuals he had demanded—these had been flung into prison by their own government —but two others had come to Avignon. Moreover, he found these men arrogantly on the defensive, ready to justify everything Florence had done on the basis of the crimes and injustices committed by the Legates. Then and there Gregory pronounced against the city his terrible interdict. Furthermore, he excommunicated the Eight of War ruling the Republic and fifty notables. Among the latter was Catherine's friend, Niccolò Soderini.

To be excommunicated was to experience literally the awfulness of being an outcast from society. The person thus sentenced could participate in no service of the Church. Indeed, every right was blotted out. Not only could all his goods be seized, but he himself could be sold into slavery. No one need pay him his just debts. No Christian could give him aid.

Considering the number of her enemies and rivals, therefore, it was no wonder Florence swiftly felt the effect of the Pope's pronouncement. It was made the excuse for snatching her property and crushing her trade all over Europe. Facing complete ruin, the Florentines sped a message to the one person they believed might help them. To Catherine Benincasa they sent the request that she personally be the mediator between themselves and the Head of the Church.

Faced by this enormous responsibility, she prayed for guidance. Indeed, so intense and continuous these days was her inward life that often an ecstatic condition would come upon her while she was in the midst of dictation. Stefano Maconi's first terror of this manifestation swiftly changed to reverent acceptance of a mystery. But he was profoundly troubled about her state of health. Suffering both pain and weakness, she often had to spend hours upon her couch.

The young man took Neri aside one day and said: "Brother, how can our Mamma contemplate a three weeks' journey to Provence? She eats nothing except the wafer of the Eucharist. She is ill. Do you not fear for her?"

"Yes," replied the other slowly, "yet strength comes to her for all she has to do. Explain this I cannot. Yet so it is. She can bear without weariness more than any of us. Wait and see."

Without being aware of it, the new disciple resisted the idea of Catherine's accepting the invitation of Florence. He hated the thought of parting from her so soon. When Fra Raimondo wrote that her letters were well received by Gregory, Stefano with reluctance saw determination gather in Catherine's mind.

At Easter time when the peach blossoms flung a veil along garden walls and olive trees were like a mist of silver-grey, Catherine made her resolution. She wrote to Florence that she would serve the city as mediator and go to Avignon. Stefano heard the letter with a feeling of bitter loss. In this tremendous undertaking he could have no share.

One day as he sat writing Catherine looked at him with a glance of sparkling gaiety. "My dear son," said she, "I have happy news to tell thee. Thy dearest wish is to be granted."

Wonderingly he regarded her. "But, *Mamma mia*, I know not myself what is my dearest wish."

She smiled. "Look in thy heart and see."

After a pause he answered in his slow and simple fashion: "I have but one great desire. It is to remain always close to thee."

Again she laughed happily. "That is to be granted."

Stefano flushed. It was marvellous news, but how could it be? Surely there were social conventions which must not be offended. How could Catherine manage such a thing? Finding her eyes fixed on him, he blushed more deeply still. For he saw that she was reading his every thought and that she scorned such puerile ideas.

Gently, however, knowing that he was new to the beautiful freedom of the Fellowship, Catherine said, "My son, thou art to accompany me to Avignon. I have need of thee. For Neri who goes with us as far as Florence may be sent ahead. Fear not! Many persons will go on that journey."

It was early in May, 1376, when she set forth. Her companions were Neri, three Mantellate, Fra Bartolommeo and Stefano Maconi. The latter had one morning brought his mother, Madonna Giovanna, to see Catherine and have her mind set at rest regarding her son's new life. Now, with all his rich clothes exchanged for sober garb, his horsemanship humbled by the slow pace of a mule, his sword no longer at his side, the dashing young man scarcely recognized himself. He hardly blamed the street boys—the very ones who used to cheer him as he fought—for running after him with their scornful cry, "Caterinato! Caterinato!"

But he was happy and full of boyish excitement. He loved the wildness of hills and forests along the way and the roadsides brilliant with early poppies. What could be more beautiful than May in Tuscany? Or what more glorious an adventure than this expedition? A jousting match—with Peace for the prize and prayers for weapons! "Truly we are a *Bella Brigata!*" he cried to Neri.

When in the late afternoon the party caught sight of the towers of Florence, Stefano's joy knew no bounds. Catherine, laughing at his felicity, roused herself from thought to point out the great red dome of the cathedral and Giotto's tower, the tower of the Palazzo Publico, and of the Bargello where the ruler lived. And so presently they came to the southern gate of the city. And there they found an enormous deputation come to welcome them. All the guilds of the city were represented and with glad demonstrations they greeted Catherine Benincasa, the peacemaker, the Heaven-sent emissary.

Through the Porta Romana the escort led her past tall, frowning houses and down a street which dropped directly to the Ponte Vecchio and the Arno. Then through a roughly paved lane they went on to Niccolò Soderini's substantial palace on the river bank. Excommunicated though he was, this rich bourgeois was not made to suffer in his own city where, indeed, all were sharing in some degree the same Papal punishment. He was there to welcome them all and bid the travellers come in to a repast of partridge, veal pasty, salad, cheese and wine.

Catherine, however, as was her wont, went directly to the room prepared for her and knelt in prayer. It was in the front of the house on the second floor. When, at last, she rose from her knees and went to the window, it was to see the fiery sunset glow behind sweeping Tuscan hills and, across the Arno, a pattern of towers and roof-tops. Her eyes dwelt on the campanile of Santa Maria Novella, the Dominican church where she had first seen Fra Raimondo da Capua. As she looked her entire being was filled with one desire—to bring peace to this unfortunate city.

Meanwhile, after their repast, Neri and Stefano wandered arm and arm about the town. The former took his friend straight to the narrow, winding street where stood the sombre house of stone where

Dante once had lived. From there they threaded their way into the cathedral square.

Stefano's eyes dilated to observe approaching a strange procession. "Behold," he cried, "a city stricken by the inderdict, a city in despair!"

An endless file of figures dressed in black—men and women singing psalms and beating their breasts in sorrow—passed before the blank face of the Duomo. Behind them walked men who at every step brought down upon their naked backs the leather whips they carried. Flagellants and penitents! Every hour of the day while they remained there the Sienese encountered these mourners. For now not one single service of the Church was held. No priest heard the confessions of sinners. No Mass was offered. And affliction filled every corner of the city.

In the process of achieving her purpose—thoroughly to inform herself about Florentine affairs—Catherine renewed all her former friendships and made a dozen new ones. Among the most influential of these relationships were with Buonaccorso di Lapa, a member of the Signoria; Angelo Ricasoli, whose family name still clings to a wide avenue; Monna Luadamia, member of the powerful house of Strozzi. Her warmest friends, however, aside from the Soderini, were Francesco Pippini, the tailor, his wife, Monna Agnese and the Canigiani family.

Between Catherine and the younger son of the latter household sprang up a peculiar sympathy. Barduccio Canigiani, cultivated and charming, possessed an intense spiritual ardour. It illuminated his sensitive face and emphasized his physical frailty. In him the Mantellata divined an extraordinarily pure flame of truth and love. And the moment his fine dark eyes fell upon her face the youth had no other wish than to offer his life for her service.

Between conferences with the Archbishop and talks with notables Catherine was exchanging letters with Fra Raimondo. She had written to ask him if he approved her sending Neri on ahead of her to Avignon and now he replied in the affirmative. Therefore, before many days were past, Neri got himself ready to depart, equipped with a letter from Catherine to the Holy Father. It was an honour, of course, to be so trusted. Yet, as he faced his lonely journey and his weighty responsibility, the young man could not help envying Stefano Maconi who could travel with the little Mamma all the way.

Catherine knew perfectly well what Neri was feeling. To comfort him she managed by speeding messenger to send him a letter at Pisa before he took his ship. Reading it, he glowed in a renewed sense of the glorious Fellowship to which he was privileged to belong. However cruel and mad the world, they had that happy little castle of the spirit all to themselves. Cordially received by all Catherine's friends in Pisa, the messenger was sent on his way warmed and heartened.

Toward the end of May, Catherine herself set out for the Papal court with the *Brigata* enlarged to twenty-three. Among the additions were the three Buonconti brothers, her former hosts in Pisa. The travellers went overland northwards by Prato and Pistoia to Bologna. Then they turned west to avoid the mountains, and thence into Provence.

All the long journey Stefano Maconi was dreaming of their destination. He wished he had Neri to talk to and to read for him a piece he had copied out in Siena and brought with him. He had never forgotten the young poet's recitation of Folgore's hunting verse and now he longed to listen to an equally dramatic rendition of Petrarch's denunciation of Avignon. Lacking Neri, Stefano one evening persuaded Father Bartolommeo to read the diatribe aloud.

The party were spending the night as guests of a lonely monastery along the way. As they gathered after the simple repast in a little arbour overlooking a deep gorge filled with tumbled rocks and greenery, Father Bartolommeo stood before them and in a sonorous voice read the passionate words.

"Everything good has gone to pieces there; first liberty, then peace, joy, hope, faith and love. Immense losses to the soul! But in the realm of avarice this is accounted no loss, as long as the revenues do not diminish. There the future life is counted as a fable. All that is said about hell, the resurrection of the body, the Day of Judgment, the Crucifixion—all, all are fables and mere idiocies. Truth is held to be madness there, abstinence absurd, shame shameful, sins of incontinence as proofs of broadmindedness. The more stained a life is, the higher it is esteemed and fame increases by crime."

When the reader had finished, an appalled silence hung over the group. Those simple, good folk,

Cecca Gori and Lisa, held up their hands in horror at this description. With one voice they cried, "Truly, Avignon cannot be so evil as this picture!"

Catherine flung back her head. "It doth appear more evil because it should be the very seat of goodness," she cried. "That is a garden choked with weeds and with wilted flowers which have a smell of vile decay! They poison and rot the ground. Oh, my sons and daughters, send from your hearts at every moment thoughts of the beautiful love of the living Christ! Only so will the work of demons in these poor misguided souls be overcome!"

Stefano Maconi felt a thrilling challenge in these words. Each member of that party, he reflected, was like a soldier martialling his thoughts against the enemy. To be aware of him under every fine disguise, to hate and fight the evil, but never the person—that was the task. He felt tremendously ready. When, at last, they entered the boat which was to take them up the Rhone, his heart was filled with excitement. This little company was advancing upon the most potent court in all Europe! Would it triumph? Looking at Catherine's face as she bent over the reedy water, he could not doubt the issue.

Flat and green were the brief banks of the river. Fishermen's huts, overhung by shining poplars, crept close to the shore and far behind and above them rose the steeps. As the galley slowly crawled against the rushing current everyone eagerly watched both sides of the stream.

Suddenly Stefano cried out, "Look, friends, we approach the city!" Fronting the Rhone ran the mediæval walls and over them rose forty towers and spires.

After they had passed along almost the entire length of the city, Father Bartolommeo pointed out across the river a great square tower standing all alone. "That was built by Philip the Fair of France," said he, "the king who first brought the Popes to Babylon. It guards the bridge, the old bridge of Saint Bénézet."

Suddenly Catherine stood up. Toward the highest point of Avignon she flung out her hand without a word. There, towering against the sky on the summit of the rock of the Doms, stood a massive edifice of grey stone, formidable as a fortress and topped by crennelated towers—the château of the French Popes. A sense of its impregnable might smote with chill every heart but one. Catherine faced it undaunted. In a voice low but distinct she said, "If ye have faith, ye shall say unto this mountain, 'Remove hence to yonder place' and it shall remove!"

Now as the boat swung toward the shore, the passengers fixed their attention upon the bridge. For along its crowded causeway swept a stream of vivid life. Sober monks were jostled by knights in armour and by pages, brilliantly cloaked and capped. Dusty travellers were passing into the city and Abbots in vermilion capes were riding out to their fine villas across the Rhone. Pedlars with packs upon their backs, farmers bearing loaded baskets, ladies in plumed hats, swaggering gentlemen—all hurried or sauntered along the highway above the swirling water. Amid the shouts and buzz of talk there

floated down the rollicking songs of student bands.
These could be seen frisking arm in arm while they
carolled ribald ditties in mock of sacred chants. All
the colour, luxury and merriment, the lusty impu-
dence and fascination of the Provençal city were
flaunted there on the Bridge of Saint Bénézet this
eighteenth day of June.

Fra Bartolommeo's voice in Stefano's ear roused
him from his absorbed staring. "*Ecco!* Dost thou
see Neri, Father Raimondo and the Master awaiting us on shore?"

There they were, crowding to the water's edge—
all the friends who had preceded them to Avignon.
And as the boat was made fast there took place under the grim old walls such a clasping of hands, such
an exchange of greetings, questions, salutations and
introductions; such a jolly confusion of movement
and speech; such laughter—that every bit of weariness and doubt vanished from the travellers' faces.
After all, despite dangers and difficulties, the Fellowship was meeting once more, miraculously united
in this strange land!

Until she saw him again Catherine had hardly
been aware how much she had missed delle Vigne.
His perception and judgment, she reflected swiftly,
were unequalled by anyone else in the group. After
an affectionate word with Neri and Father Tantucci
she turned to her confessor and walked beside him
through the guarded gate and up the narrow street.
Most of the others lagged a bit in eager talk.
Stefano with his hand on Neri's shoulder plied him
with questions. Through the crowded city walked

the little company, the priest and Catherine at its head.

As they came to the main street they had to halt. For a party on horseback was sweeping toward them. A horn's bright note, the falconer galloping ahead with cages swung from his saddle announced a return from the hunt. Slowed down by a train of wagons in the road, the riders passed by slowly. Lovely ladies and fine gentlemen, portly Cardinals and young gallants—all splendid in hunting array —turned their heads in one direction and wonderingly stared.

Who could she be, those glances seemed to ask, this young Dominican boasting so large a suite? Was she come thinking to redeem Avignon—this bit of human insignificance? The thought drew laughter. Delicious, careless Avignon, radiant child of pleasure—never would it don the sober robe of piety! Joyously the cavalcade clattered on its way.

Fra Raimondo waved an accusing hand. "Such are the folk who strive to alter the Holy Father's resolution. They make nothing of his announced intention to return to Rome. And, indeed, he talks of it no further. But to thee he may say otherwise."

In a few moments the travellers had arrived at their destination. For their use had been assigned the house of a Cardinal no longer residing in the city. Its size and accommodations permitted the entire party to stay under one roof. This in itself was matter for mutual congratulations. Their entrance was followed by a great running up and down, the jolly bustle of getting settled. But Catherine, with a parting smile for this liveliness, went straight to the little chapel in one wing of the mansion. There she remained for hours.

Indeed, for two days the Mantellata was closeted in isolation. She dictated no letters. She saw only Neri and Father Raimondo. Then, prepared by their information, equipped with the serene power of spiritual contact, she set out with her confessor for her first visit to the Papal palace. They did not have far to walk. Yet already news of the arrival of a holy virgin from a distant part of Italy drew many folk into the narrow lanes to watch her pass. From Gothic windows giving on the street ladies leaned and murmured, laughing behind their jewelled fingers. With amused confidence they predicted a speedy withdrawal of this defeated little reformer. But there were some who looked upon that face and felt dismay.

Although she walked swiftly with head erect, Catherine was aware of those smirking faces, and with almost physical repugnance sensed the vicious life which encrusted the religious treasure of the city. As they reached the great château, she raised her eyes to one of its lofty turrets and mourned anew that this structure, so magnificent in aspect, could not lift a beacon light of holy purpose for all mankind to follow.

Between the massive doors Fra Raimondo guided his companion past guardsmen and officials into the anteroom. Presently they were bidden to enter the audience hall. It was the loftiest chamber Catherine had ever seen. Murals and hangings coloured the neutral walls of stone. In the foreground flunkeys and clerks were bustling in and out.

But at the far end of the vast apartment a stately and brilliant tableau was set and waiting. Robes of Bishops, Cardinals and Abbots made a tapestry of purple, scarlet, gold and white. The gorgeous figures stood on either side of a dais and upon this, smothered in his robes and cape of lace, sat Gregory Eleventh.

He was not tall. His posture expressed bodily weakness, his face a vacillating, yet stubborn character. Yet as Catherine knelt before him, her heart was glad. Those intelligent eyes looked kindly down upon her. Purity and love of goodness marked the brow and mouth.

In the silence that followed the Papal blessing, the hearts of those assembled prelates skipped a beat. This humble maiden from afar, received in state by the great Prince of the Church! Was there not special meaning in the scene? Apprehensive eyes fastened on the face toward which Gregory bent so eagerly. What had this young Tertiary come to do in Avignon?

Chapter Seven

BEFORE Catherine Benincasa entered the audience hall of the Pope, she had been merely an object of curiosity in Avignon. From that moment on she became a figure of profound consequence. News of what had occurred during that session was spread far and wide by those indignant and frightened prelates who had been present. Throughout the city and across the river at Villeneuve the great households buzzed with amazed and furious comment. How dared she—an ignorant nobody from afar!

Ah, but she *had* dared! The key in which the celebrated interview had been conducted struck the onlookers from the first as disturbing. Yet that key had been altogether quiet. Catherine's attitude, the sweet humility of her phrases assured the Holy Father both of her reverence for him and of her

182

gratitude to be in his presence. Smoothly Fra Raimondo translated the gracious Tuscan into Latin. For Gregory understood no syllable of the Italian language.

Expectantly the Pope leaned forward. With cheek resting on his hand and eyes fixed on the eloquent face, he listened rather to the musical voice than to the facts presented by the interpreter. Catherine told him of affairs in Florence and of the real desire there among the people for peace with the Church.

When she had finished, Gregory said gently: "All thou hast done is right and good. I shall trust this affair entirely to you." A murmur and movement among the Cardinals deflected his attention to their astonished protest and he added gravely, "Only forget not the dignity of the Church."

Catherine spoke eloquently of the Crusade and then swept on to the need of reform within ecclesiastical circles. Still supplicating, but now impassioned, she pleaded for the abolishments of evils in general and especially of those rooted about the Holy See.

Gregory's rejoinder was vague agreement. Thereupon his interlocutor became explicit. To the fury of those dignitaries ranged on either side of her, to the embarrassment of delle Vigne, who hesitated to repeat that intrepid censure, Catherine launched upon an incisive description of the corruption at Avignon. She spared no detail.

Gregory's slender hands clenched upon the carved chair-arms. His eyes passed swiftly left and right across those leaning faces of rage and consternation. At the exhortation's finish he sank back and summoned a slight, derogatory smile. In a voice tinged with irony he asked, "How long hath my daughter been in our city?"

Fra Raimondo was obliged to answer, "Two days, your Holiness."

This exchange Catherine understood. She comprehended, also, the meaning of the Pope's nod and the almost imperceptible French shrug with which he gravely said, "It is as I supposed."

At this all gentleness, all humility, all supplication left the young Dominican. It was not a woman standing there amid the pomp of churchly persons. It was a flame—beautiful and terrible—a flame that burned away the implication of her ignorance.

"To the honour of God Almighty I make bold to say that while abiding in my own city where I was born I have perceived more vileness of sin committed in the Roman Curia than they themselves have perceived who have committed and do daily commit such sins in this court."

Before the knowledge in her eyes the Cardinals shrank back, the Pope's smile vanished. Silence and trepidation swept over that assembly. It was as if the heavens had opened and a Voice had spoken from on high. An awful memory arose like a picture before the eyes of everyone—the Christ in sublime wrath against evil, driving the moneychangers from the Temple of the Lord.

Catherine had sunk upon her knees. After the long hush, Gregory's voice, altered by emotion, was heard to reiterate his trust in the Mantellata and then he gave his blessing. No more complete triumph was conceivable. Fearfully the Cardinals and Bishops watched the small figure pass swiftly from the audience hall. Hers was a power they could not fathom, an influence they knew not how to combat. But in the new assurance of Gregory's glance they could gauge the strength of their adversary.

Not that day did the Fellowship learn the details of Catherine's reception at the château. She was closeted in silent meditation all afternoon, and Fra Raimondo merely stated that the occasion had been most propitious. To while away the time till they might consult their leader about the letters just arrived, Neri and Stefano set forth on a stroll about the town. The former had learned it thoroughly and began the expedition with the view from the plâteau beyond the Papal palace.

"Clement Fifth it was made the *palazzo* so magnificent," mused Neri, gazing at its massive outline. "He had the frescoes painted on the walls of court and hall and he set the fashion of pomp and splendour. Dost thou know how large is the palace retinue?"

Stefano snatched off his peaked cap to let the breeze blow through his thick brown curls. "Mayhap if cooks and servants be counted in, there are a hundred."

Neri laughed scornfully. "No, four times that number! The physician of his Holiness is Francesco Cassini from Siena and he hath told me much of what goes on. Gregory Eleventh likes not the luxury about him. But some among his prelates, in imitation of the château, live like princes and possess many servitors and men-at-arms and secretaries. Costly furniture have they, too, and rare wines at table—like that ruby liquid made here called 'Château-Neuf-des Papes.' Also, Stefano, ladies fair of face and well versed in every art but purity dwell in certain households of the clergy. I myself through Messer Cassini have been present at more than one *festa* in these mansions and I know."

The two had begun to descend the hill toward the river. Between his teeth Stefano said: "Small wonder our Republics rebel against such leaders! But the Holy Father himself is altogether good, is it not true?"

"It is true. He is a scholar and a cultured man of excellent life. At eighteen he was made a Cardinal and is not fifty yet. Were he not so surrounded by men determined to serve France and his king Charles Fifth, he would ere this have made things different here. He lacks conviction and yields too much weight to the temporal possessions of the Church. Yet, here in this serene and joyous place, one cannot blame him for preferring it to the turbulence of Rome."

The June sun, so soft on grey stone walls, glinted brilliantly from the surface of the Rhone. Between towers and roof-tops could be seen, colourful and crowded as ever, the bridge of Saint Bénézet. A glimpse of it was quite enough to lift those youthful spirits and their eyes met in the same happy thought. It was fascinating to see the world and savour this jolly old city of Provence.

Stefano, who was never unsettled as Neri was by delight in external things, cried out: "Why need there be evil in Avignon when sky and river are so gay? If God directs the senses there is no harm in them, but only learning. This day makes me gladder than does wine. Let us walk across the bridge and watch the folk pass by."

Yielding to the contagion of high spirits, Neri led the way. They passed shops where lacemakers were busy fashioning ecclesiastical fineries and other shops of metal workers who hammered delicate ornaments for altars and rich homes. Then through the portal of the bridge they emerged upon its floor and into the swirl of human traffic. At the little chapel built above a pier not far from shore they paused. There lay the bones of the doughty dreamer who two hundred years before, indomitable in face of obstacles, had built the highway across the river—good little Saint Bénézet himself. Halfway across they paused again. Leaning over the stone coping, Neri pointed out the lush, flat meadow islanded in mid-stream and the young men laughed to see a group of youths and maidens there below, dancing in a circle and pelting each other with marguerites.

Intoxicated by this scene, Neri cried, "Oh, these are jubilant folk! One day of *festa* I saw them— young and old—dancing on the bridge itself. They play a sort of game and sing a sweet and foolish ditty which in their language goes like this ———"

Unmindful of the passers-by, the young man gaily chanted, *"Sur le pont d'Avignon, l'on y danse, l'on y danse! Sur le pont d'Avignon l'on y danse tout en ronde!"*

As the singer finished, he felt himself clapped upon the shoulder and heard a laughing voice in his ear. *"Bon,* monsieur! For a foreigner you have done good justice to our song, Messer Ranieri di Landoccio!"

An elegant youth with features of chiselled vigour stood beside him and Neri recognized the secretary to one of the French cardinals. Many delightful hours before Catherine's arrival had Neri spent with him in discussing poetry and philosophic teachings. Cordially, despite his confusion, he presented his acquaintance to Stefano Maconi.

"You must both return with me at once," cried the stripling eagerly. He spoke Italian with a Frenchman's staccato accent. "A group gathers even now at our mansion to see the Greek manuscript my lord hath bought from a peddling Jew. It is said to be a priceless treasure."

Neri's eyes gleamed with interest. Linking arms, he walked between the others along the noisy thoroughfare. "It will please me, indeed, to see this prize. But I do wonder much about this new learning from the Ancients. When we have mastered it—what then? Will it change our faith?"

Stefano smiled at the ever-present conflict in his friend's sensitive mind. Said he: "Thy faith should stand the test of ancient lore, *mio caro.* Surely we now know much the Greeks could not understand before Christ came to earth."

The quiet words impressed both his companions and Neri squeezed his friend's arm. "Ah, Stefano, would I had thy simple wisdom. Thou fearest nothing—not even the temptation of the mind."

Nevertheless, when a little later they were escorted into the vast, cool palace of the Cardinal and were presented to a distinguished company, Neri found his friend's indifference strange. How could Stefano look upon that yellow parchment, preserved so miraculously through ages and brought so far— that parchment inscribed with Heaven knew what marvels of thought—and feel no thrill? Before Neri had had half enough of all the talk about the script and what it might prove to be, Stefano was pulling at his sleeve.

"The sand has all run out from yonder hourglass and it waxes late afternoon. Likely our little Mamma may have need of us," Maconi urged. And after the two had taken their leave, he added: "Thou knowest ambassadors are expected from Florence to sue for peace and clemency from the Holy Father. There may be news for us at our house."

News there was, indeed, but of no favourable kind. Delle Vigne and Catherine received the secretaries and told them what had happened. The Florentines had passed a new tax upon the clergy in their region—a gesture of defiance, not of peace—and Catherine felt her mission was betrayed.

Two days later at the château she said this candidly. This time she was received in a private room which looked over the river and was reached by a marble staircase. A green carpet patterned in red roses lay upon the floor and chairs draped in yellow damask offered informal comfort to the visitors.

Mournful and sympathetic were the eyes Gregory turned upon his visitor. Through Fra Raimondo he said to her: "The Florentines do mock both thee and me. Either the ambassadors come not at all, or if they come they will not be furnished with essential authority."

So dire a possibility was inadmissible to the ardent Mantellata. Yet when nearly a week went by and that delegation failed to arrive, she dictated a letter to the Eight of War at Florence.

I protest strongly to you, if it is true what is said here, that you have imposed a levy on the clergy. . . . Do not put me to shame and reproach. What could result but disgrace and confusion if I tell him one thing and you do the opposite? I implore you not to let it happen again.

I have talked to the Holy Father. . . . After a half-hour's conversation with him he ended by telling me that he is ready to receive you as his children and to do what would seem to me the best. It is impossible that the Holy Father give you any other answer before the arrival of your ambassadors. I am astonished that they are not yet here. As soon as they come I shall go to see them and see again the Holy Father and inform you of events. But you have spoiled all by increasing the tax. Put an end to this levy then, for the love of God.

On July sixth, before that protest could reach Florence either by land or sea, a new government was elected. This body reported to Avignon that it would shortly send deputies and, expectant of they knew not what, the Fellowship awaited their arrival. Meanwhile the world of fashion and power around the Papal See drew close to examine this maid from Siena and discover what she was really like.

Lovely ladies came to call upon her. One, the Pope's sister, was truly reverent in her interest and had many sympathetic talks alone with the young Tertiary. But the others merely came from curiosity and hid their amused contempt of her and all the Fellowship behind a mask of courtesy. Lisa and Alessa with lively interest examined their tight basques, their slashed-up petticoats and tall veiled hats like cornucopias. Fra Raimondo enjoyed their cultivated comments. But Catherine, for whom they came, held them at the utmost distance.

"Do you not know," she would cry when they were gone, "what these women really are? It is as if I could smell the sin that clings about them."

To her any other type of visitor was more endurable—even the inevitable incursion of sceptical theologians hoping to prove her either fool or devil. At Avignon the questioners who came were three in number and were armed with authority from the château to make their examination of her faith.

Stefano Maconi received these visitors in the hall and stiffened at the hauteur of their bearing. To hear their peremptory command, "Tell Caterina we would speak to her!" was to long to turn them out upon the street.

Presently Fra Raimondo brought her down the

stairs. Father Tantucci, Alessa and Cecca followed close behind and after the formal greetings everyone sat down.

"We are come from *Il Papa*," said the spokesman to Catherine, "to find out if the Florentines have really sent you to him as is pretended. If they did so, it seems strange they had no man capable of such an important mission. If they did not, then it seems queer a little woman like you would dare discuss these matters with the Holy Father."

Stefano was so angry that he half rose from his seat. But Catherine's eyes betrayed a suppressed smile. Indeed, she often wondered why more was not said about a woman's doing what she did. She answered calmly and led them to their real point which was the challenge of her doctrine. She outlined the substance of it and spoke frankly of her visions. Replying to their questions about her habits, she admitted that she could not eat, but added that she advocated no rigours of penance for another.

Hour after hour drew on. The three theologians seemed fascinated by the exhibition of her knowledge. Now and then, whether moved by indignation or the fear that Catherine's orthodoxy would be inadequate, the Master tried to answer in her place. But the prelates waved him aside. "Let her reply," they said. "She satisfies us much better than you know how to do."

Indeed, when at dusk the inquisitors took their leave, their manner toward their victim had completely changed. They expressed their grateful ad-

miration and humbly begged leave to be received
again.

Next morning a Papal messenger came to fetch
Catherine to the château. The great Prince received
her in his cabinet of work within the Tour des
Anges and never had his manner been more intimate and kind.

"I regret the persecution thou hadst to endure
yesterday," declared Gregory. "Those dignitaries
went against my counsel and if others come thou
mayst with my consent shut the door of thy house
upon their noses. However"—here he leaned forward with an expression of surprised satisfaction—
"hear this. Last night these same men came to me
and said that never in their lives had they met anyone at once so humble and so illuminated. This word
they will spread about to advance thy standing here.
They are now thy friends."

Smiling, Catherine declared that nothing mat-
tered less than her own prestige in Avignon and
passed swiftly to the question of Florentine politics.
She declared her certainty that despite the government the people themselves wanted only justice and
the Pope's return to Rome and were at heart
obedient.

That same morning Neri and Stefano, returning
from sending out a number of couriers, near Saint-
Didier encountered Francesco Cassini, the Pope's
physician. Thrusting his hands in the embroidered
belt of his long red mantle, Cassini said: "Our citizen, Caterina, has made us proud. Let me tell you
this—if you put on one balance of the scale the

knowledge of those three prelates who questioned her and on the other balance all the Roman court, the former would outweigh the latter. That she could win their admiration is triumph, indeed. For had Caterina not been solid they would have found her weakness out."

"You are surprised, Messer Francesco," returned Stefano quietly, "but not I. There is not her like on earth today."

During the next weeks discriminating persons throughout the city came to the same opinion. For they saw this woman tried by public humiliation of the most aggravated character and remain untouched by wounded pride.

At last from Florence the two ambassadors arrived. But with insulting manner, they refused to treat with Catherine, denied her power to serve their city, repulsed her offer to interview the Pope in their behalf. Rebuff could not have been more cruel. True, the Holy Father in his turn snubbed these men by denying them a hearing and their parleys with his representative came to naught. But that only seemed to make the peacemaker's position more absurd. All the town rocked with laughter. They said it served the tradesman's daughter right for her presumption and hoped Gregory would now shake off her influence.

Hardly a member of the Fellowship but felt the slap and shuddered at the ridicule. They hated to go out upon the street. Therefore, they were the more struck with Catherine's attitude. Incapable of caring about what happened to herself, she suffered only for the cause of peace and justice. But she suffered in silence. Clearly she recognized that the new Florentine party wanted war and that their embassy was but a blind. Therefore she ceased all effort to interfere; sent no letter to Florence and made no further overtures to its delegates. This magnificent dismissal of a lost cause freed her energies for the two issues which still promised success—the Crusade and the Pope's return to Rome.

Gregory's sister, Comtesse de Valentinois, was one of those who admired Catherine's display of dignity. She implored the Mantellata to visit her, received her in much state and presented her to Cardinal Bartolommeo Prignano, Archbishop of Bari. He was a Neapolitan and with him Catherine spoke of Queen Giovanna and the possibility of her supporting the Crusade. Though brusque in manner, the Cardinal showed every sign of respect and courtesy to the celebrated Dominican—quite as if attempting to atone for the hostility of his French colleagues.

This was a conversation pregnant for the future. While it was going on the Countess had a word with Father delle Vigne. "Father," she began, "in all reverence I ask of you a favour. May I be permitted to behold Caterina in her divine trance after the Eucharist? I know nothing would so quicken my faith in our human power to reach God."

Her earnestness persuaded Fra Raimondo to consent and he promised to summon her when it seemed suitable. But, although correct in his estimate of that sincerity, the priest would never have granted this permission had he known better the secular world of Avignon. For behind the metal-studded oaken doors of some of these great Gothic houses, that which he held sacred as the Holy Script was the subject of frivolous gossip.

Nothing was discussed with more levity, than the ecstatic trances of Catherine Benincasa. They were a new sensation, a favourite joke. Everyone debated whether or not she was a fakir and those who had never stolen into church or chapel to observe her at first hand were at a disadvantage. Such a plight was the lot of Élys de Turenne, the young wife of the Pope's nephew and so unused was the lovely worldling to any lack of supremacy that she was determined by hook or crook to see the Sienese at prayers. The moment she heard her relative in marriage was to witness the phenomenon she insisted on being a member of the party.

One Sunday morning as the members of Catherine's household were about to pass into the chapel Father delle Vigne beckoned to Stefano Maconi. "Go to the *palazzo* of the Holy Father," he commanded, "and find his sister there. Tell her Caterina will receive Communion shortly."

Wonderingly Stefano obeyed. By this time officials and men-at-arms about the château knew all of Catherine's suite and gave them leave to go and come unchallenged. Maconi was told the lady he sought was hearing Mass at the palace chapel. Hardly had he put foot into the crowded place of worship when the Countess recognized the tall young man and stepped to his side.

"My son," she whispered, "what dost thou wish of me?"

Hearing his message, she signalled to several women standing near and at once they followed the young secretary out and down the street to Catherine's house. Stefano, who had often seen young Madame de Turenne riding her white palfrey beside some gay cavalier, wondered whether her presence in that group meant she had a heart that longed for good.

Soon he was to know. In the chapel just behind Catherine the young woman knelt reverently and seemed much moved when the Mantellata after communicating sank forward, rigid and unconscious. At the end of the service Madame de Turenne on her way out thanked Fra Raimondo sweetly. Stefano, Neri and Alessa remained there waiting for Catherine to regain her normal senses and for a sight of that lovely look of pure joy with which she did so. It came. But when she rose to her feet it was with a cry of anguish. "My foot! It is wounded!"

All three friends helped bear Catherine upstairs to her couch. When they took off the soft cloth sandal she was wearing they found it filled with blood. Instantly Maconi understood what had happened and furiously faced the others.

"It was she—that devil de Turenne with her sweet cat's face! She hath stabbed this precious foot with a sharp, long needle—kneeling just behind her and wishing to try the reality of her trance. O cursed wretch! She came here only for so vile a purpose!"

Feebly Catherine smiled at his violence. "Curse the evil, my son, not the woman. Perchance she may now believe that the senses are not so real as she had supposed."

While Alessa and Lisa bathed the wound Fra Bartolommeo came in and after learning what had happened, said in bewilderment: "Sweetest Mamma, it is so strange how the cycle of persecution is repeated. Four times have learned men come to thee with hostile tests of thy faith. Twice hath thy foot been stabbed. Why is it so?"

The glowing dark eyes suddenly filled with grief. "Because of my sins, Father. I have been given such infinite love and I fail so often!"

Stefano, who was leaving the room, said in stupefaction to Neri in the hall. "She means what she hath said, our dearest Mamma. She believes she is a sinner. Canst thou imagine such a thing?"

Neri replied simply: "Her goal is perfection. Remember that, as we have just witnessed, she is entirely transported to the kingdom of Heaven for part of each day, and therefore knows immaculate goodness as doth no one else." In awe-stricken silence the two young men sounded one another's eyes.

For the next two days Catherine remained propped upon her pillows. But she managed to dictate two letters to the Pope which were like bugle notes. Saying to him, "Courage, my Father, be a man!" she tried to answer his doubts regarding his return to Rome. She besought him to do right, trust God for the rest and banish fear. Well she knew that as she played upon his aspiration, so did his relatives and the French Cardinals play upon his timidity. They told him any lie which would prevent him from leaving the place where they were so content. The Pontiff's answer to her missives was a summons to the château on the Doms and as soon as she could walk she set out once more to bolster up Gregory's collapsing will.

That it was her fate to do so aroused her sense of humour. With her persuasive, loving air, she remarked that morning with a smile, "Why do you, a Pope, seek counsel of me who am but a wretched little woman?"

Gregory, without answering the question directly, plunged into a long recital of those prophecies of disaster which he had been told would follow his departure from Avignon—accident, treachery, death. These torturing images combined with his own reluctance to cope with tumultuous Rome to oppose the urge of his conscience.

Catherine listened and her eyes looked deep into his soul. Finally she said in a tone of vibrating authority, "You know what once you promised God! Now keep your vow!"

Pale grew the Pope's face. He opened his lips to speak. Then he fell back in his chair and covered his eyes with his long white fingers. "It is true," he gasped. "It is true. To bring the Curia to Rome —that promise I made and have not kept and must." Suddenly he leaned forward and stared at

Catherine. "How couldst thou know that? To none but God did I speak."

She made no answer. She looked at him as if she were pouring her courage, her knowledge, her capacity for sacrifice into his very veins. And before she left Gregory that day he had given her his sacred word. Come what might, he would return to Rome.

So firmly did he make public this intention that the Cardinals began to think he really meant it. Word of this peril was sent to King Charles Fifth and that sovereign immediately sent his brother to persuade the Pope from so foolish a purpose. With fanfare of trumpets and brilliant escort of armoured knights, the Duc d'Anjou came riding to the Rhone.

Leaving his wife and her ladies at Villeneuve to prepare the castle for the sojourn, he betook himself at once across the river to the château. It was not long, however, before he learned that to sway the will of Gregory he had first to reach the person who had stiffened it. Therefore one day an equerry with the royal arms blazoned on his shield knocked upon Catherine's door. The astounded family learned that the brother of the King of France sought for an interview with the maiden from Siena.

That first conference between the odd pair went well, but required further parley. The upshot was that one evening Catherine announced that she was going to Villeneuve for a three-day visit with the Duc and Duchesse d'Anjou. All the household gathered to watch her depart and exhibited an excited pride in odd contrast to her complete un-concern.

Alessa laughed about it. "Rank is naught to our blessed Mamma. When I remember the girl of twenty-two who asked me so many questions about the families in Siena, I marvel. Since the time when she knew but Fonte Branda and the hospitals only seven years have passed. Yet behold her now in the very centre of all that happens in the world!"

During Catherine's absence news of Italy grew worse. Florence had sent ambassadors to the Emperor of Germany, to Hungary's king and the Doges of Venice. These countries were all invited to join the League against the temporal power of the Papacy. Meanwhile in defence of that power, the fighting Cardinal, Robert of Geneva, with a host of Breton soldiers was carrying on a bloody war against the rebel cities all through the north of Italy.

Catherine heard this news with more equanimity than if she had not gone to Villeneuve. Although she had not been able to convince the Duc d'Anjou that the Papal See should be re-established at Rome, she had made a friend of the French Prince. Moreover, he had been completely captivated by her plan for the Crusade and had promised to raise an army to be sent against the infidels.

Stefano, delighted with this report, said happily to Neri: "The king's brother knew little of our Mamma if he expected to prevail against her. On one point, at least, she was certain to persuade him to her way of thought."

During these hot days of late August when the sirocco was like a furnace blast over the town, Catherine's activity seemed more than ever prodigious. She sent letters to Charles Fifth and to the King of England about the Crusade. She made new friends among churchmen and received constant visitors. Almost every day she sent some message to the Pope. One letter in particular proved important in its effect upon him. In it she said:

I implore you on the part of Christ Crucified to make haste. Use a holy deceit; that is, appear to defer the day and then go quickly and soon and you shall escape the sooner from this anguish and travail. Let us go quickly, my sweet Babbo, without any fear. If God is with you, no one else shall be against you.

It was well known that only one Cardinal, the Spaniard—Pedro de Luna—was in favour of going to Rome. The others, backed by the Pope's father and his brothers, strove with might and main against the plan and worked upon both Gregory's fear and his affections. To Catherine, praying for Gregory's strength of purpose as she knelt before the altar in her room, came a sense of mighty wings beating about those turrets and towers of the château. This ultimate combat was at its climax. But it seemed to her less one of human wills than a conflict between spiritual powers of good and evil.

Her request for a final interview with the Pontiff was granted and for the last time she passed up the stairway of the great palace. As she did so she had an impression of glaring faces, whispers like hisses, hatred of her everywhere.

Crouched in the depths of his tall arm-chair, the Ruler of Christendom looked unequal to his rôle. Catherine fully realized that before her sat only a hesitating, tortured individual. Yet she brought him no compassion. Facing that figure of abashed authority, she gave once more the impression of a resistless, living flame. What were fears or personal desires, the love of parents, the sweet comforts of this earth as compared to Eternal Truth? Nothing and less than nothing. No matter how hard the way, how bleak the future, how perilous the outcome, Christ's Vicar had no choice but to keep his word and obey the Will of God. That was what she told him. And in the end she triumphed.

At dawn on the thirteenth of September the entire household of the Fellowship was in action. The Mantellate were packing the few articles of extra clothing possessed by the members of the group. Neri, Stefano and the Buonconti brothers were about the town, arranging for the hire of boats and mules. And as they worked they wondered. The *Bella Brigata* was leaving Avignon, but would it really be today? Only if the Pope kept his given promise and actually departed. Might he not, however, delay again? There were no signs of preparation, no unusual stir along the streets.

When their duties took the young men to the river's edge, nevertheless, Stefano's sharp eyes observed an unmistakable sign. "Look! He surely goes today—and by that token we go, too!" There, hidden close to shore were the Papal galleys drawn up and waiting.

Neri turned from the gorgeously decorated boats and looked in the direction of the château. "The Father took her advice! 'A holy deceit,' truly— even as the little Mamma said in the letter I transcribed. No one has been warned. He will go suddenly."

They hurried back to inform Catherine and the others. As soon as all had breakfasted the entire Fellowship went in a body to the square before the château. But by this time the secret was out and all the city was on the run. Students, doctors, priests, fair ladies with mantles hastily flung on, clerks, nobles and tradesmen were flocking from all directions to the great palace.

Through its open gates could be seen pages and servants rushing across the court. At every moment messengers and dignitaries pushed through the crowds into the château and both within and without its sombre walls the movement and bustle of tremendous excitement grew greater from one second to another.

Unobtrusively as she was placed, Catherine was discovered by many of the people in the press. They pointed her out and to the horrified ears of the *Brigata* angry murmurs passed quickly through the throng. Everyone except that little group of strangers from Siena lamented what was taking place. Gold workers and weavers, pastry cooks and wine merchants, tailors, lawyers and clerks—all wrung their hands to know the Pope was leaving. They saw their fortunes going with him and ruin staring them in the face. Without its great Papal court, Avignon would be an empty shell. Women wept. Young men swore round oaths. And what with fear, sorrow, anger and excitement the tumult became deafening.

Suddenly it ceased. Trumpets blew and a roll of drums beat for the march of men-at-arms out of the palace gates. After them, deathly pale but resolute, stepped Gregory Eleventh. A roar of protest went up from the mob. People surged forward, lifting their clasped hands in a last plea. Comte de Beaufort, the Pope's old father, cast himself full-length, sobbing across the threshold and in the background could be seen the Cardinals openly weeping.

For an instant the impressive figure hesitated. Then, while a gasp of horror rose from one end of the square to the other, Gregory deliberately stepped over the prostrate form of his father. His lips were seen to move and what he said was afterwards set down: "It is written. Thou shalt walk upon the aspic and the basilisk."

Slowly, inevitably, like a man in a dream, he passed on across the square—the people falling back in silence—and down the lane to the Rhone. Perforce the Cardinals and officials followed after. The Babylonian Captivity was over. The Pope had left Avignon.

Swiftly the Fellowship by one concerted action closed in about their leader and began to move away from the square. But already the furious murmur of the crowd had singled her out for blame. "She has accomplished this—that Dominican Tertiary walking there—Catherine of Siena!"

It was true. For seventy years the greatest minds and hearts had striven for this end. Dante, Petrarch, Bridget of Sweden, Rienzi—statesmen, prelates, powerful lords and cities throughout Italy—all had moved heaven and earth to wedge the Papacy free from France. In vain! It remained for the maiden of Fonte Branda with her pure and patient effort to achieve the purpose. Without the compulsion of her fiery conviction, Gregory would never have scaled the opposition piled against him. Those words spoken in anger became history. It was Catherine of Siena who brought back the Pope to Rome.

The wonder of it filled the heart of each member of the Fellowship and was the subject of all their talk during the long days of travel. That very morning after the Papal party had departed, the *Brigata*, too, slid swiftly down the river to the Mediterranean shore. From their landing place they took passage on a sailboat. But the storms were so violent that the ship was almost wrecked and they had to put to shore.

In those hours of danger Catherine would cry: "What fear you? You have no need to be guardians of yourselves."

She alone was unperturbed. But so effective was her exhortation that when the ship returned to harbour, the passengers had conquered their terror and were singing the *Te Deum* in excellent form. Nevertheless, they all agreed that it was best to proceed by land.

Fra Raimondo, whose main endowment was not physical courage, said anxiously to Catherine one day: "Perhaps the Holy Father, also, is suffering from these dread storms. If he were drowned—Oh, my daughter, all the world would say the evil prophecies had been fulfilled and that he should never have left Avignon."

"What is to be will be," she replied serenely. "We have no power over the moment of death and in any case the Vicar of Christ did right to keep his word."

By mule-back the *Brigata* followed the tortuous road which had been laid out by the ancient Romans, the Via Aurelia. That beautiful, wild, rugged region, hanging above the winy sea was the very same land now called the Riviera and the highway, so smoothed now for purring motor cars, is the Grande Corniche. Then, however, there was but a broken and neglected path running along the cliffs and to travel it was wearisome and lonely beyond description.

Flowers were luxuriant and the sea as beautiful as it is today. Catherine's companions always remembered afterwards how she loved those scenes. Once she made everyone stop to examine a huge ant-hill beside the road. "These little beings," she said tenderly, "come out like us from the holy thought of God and He has put as much care in creating the insects and the flowers as the angels."

Indeed, she was gay, tireless and triumphant. When the party rested for the night at some isolated monastery she was the last one to put out her lamp. In the morning the first person to wake would see her walking at the cliff's edge or beside the sea. On the third of October they reached Varazze. The town, though desolated by the plague, was dear to Catherine because there had once lived the author of a book she loved—the famous *Legende Dorée*, containing limpid stories about all the Saints.

Into Genoa they rode the very next day and were received by the good and pious Orietta Scotti with whom Catherine had often corresponded. She found rooms for the entire *Brigata* in her large mansion which stood near the harbour. Relief and the relaxation of being once more with friends in civilization were spoiled for the travellers, however, because one by one nearly all of them fell ill. Neri, the first to succumb, ran such a fever that Stefano who was chief nurse despaired of his life.

In deep anxiety one evening he sought out Catherine and begged her to help with her miraculous, health-giving prayers. To his amazement she seemed to weigh the matter with the utmost coolness. Not having been with the Mantellata through the plague, Stefano did not realize her attitude toward death. That she considered it a blessing to anyone young or old—a blessing which only selfishness would intercept—came to him as a shock. Uncomforted, he went away to sit by Neri's bedside. As he turned and re-turned the glass of sand which marked the slow hours of the night he pondered the strangeness of Catherine's love for Neri which would so serenely let him die.

Nevertheless, next morning the physician took

one look at the patient and beckoned the weary nurse into the hall. "What has happened? I feared this young man would be dead ere this and I find him in a natural sleep and his fever broken."

Stefano's heart leaped. She did pray for her son, then! She saved him after all! He was so full of gratitude that he forgot to wonder at Catherine's power and, indeed, was not surprised at what she did for him when at last he himself became ill.

The morning after he took to his bed she came with Fra Raimondo to stand beside him. "What ails thee, Stefano?" she asked softly.

Already comforted by her presence, he looked at her out of heavy eyes and mumbled cheerfully, "They tell me I am suffering with—oh, I don't know what."

She put her cool hand on his brow and said with tender humour, "Listen to the child who says, 'They tell me I am suffering with I don't know what' and he has a violent fever!" Her eyes dwelt upon him gravely. "I do not permit thee to follow the example of the other sick ones and I order thee by holy obedience not to suffer from this malady. I wish thee to be completely cured and serve the others as usual."

Quietly then she began to talk to him about the goodness and mercy of God. A delicious sense of ease stole over him and when she had finished speaking he felt refreshed and well. "Thou hast cured me, little Mamma," he breathed. An hour later he was up, dressed and ready for work.

As little by little the sick recovered and began to

enter into the activities of the household once more, they found it had become the Mecca for all the distinguished people of Genoa. Catherine was receiving visitors almost every hour of the day. Learned doctors of law and theology, priests, professors of science and senators came from all parts of the city to pay homage to the celebrated Tertiary. They found her warm and simple. As long as they lived they remembered her lovely voice, her sunlit smile and that quality which contrasted strangely with all these attributes—a soaring of spirit to heights so unattainable as to leave everyone else a little giddy.

Unlike those casual visitors, however, Catherine's intimates were forever having this terrifying impression offset by her human sweetness, her gaiety and humour. Let any principle be at stake, nevertheless, and she was immovably austere. It was that note of rigour she sounded in two letters which Stefano wrote for her the moment he could be spared from nursing. Each was addressed to a mother—Catherine's and his own.

Before their departure from Avignon a wail had come from Monna Lapa begging Catherine to come back. The poor woman never quite grasped the fact that she, a home-loving hen, had hatched out a swan destined to float in strange waters. But in this letter her daughter made it plain that did Monna Lapa wish to be mother of her soul as well as of her body she must feel only joy in what her child was permitted to do for the glory of God.

To Madonna Giovanna, Currado Maconi's wife, she wrote in the same tone. Already she had sent from Avignon one letter to the anxious woman. Now, after an assurance that the writer herself gave Stefano a mother's tender solicitude, she dictated this reproof:

Mothers who love their children in a worldly way often say, "I do not oppose my children's wish to serve God, but they can serve the world at the same time." Such ones impose laws and rules upon the Holy Spirit. They love not their children in God, but outside God . . . and they love their bodies rather than their souls.

Thoughtfully Stefano laid down his quill and the troubled face of his yearning mother rose before him. In a flash he realized completely all the pain and sacrifice involved in true devotion to the Spirit and he saw that Catherine's willingness to pay that price made her absolutely unique. Later that day he said to Neri, as he took the convalescent for a stroll by the sea, "Our little Mamma has no other love or thought except it comes from God."

That same certainty about her was cherished by another individual—Gregory Eleventh. It hung before his consciousness all the time he lingered at Marseilles and during the dreadful voyage with the grudging Cardinals. Furious storms drove them into port time after time and every fresh start involved argument and persuasion. When finally on October eighteenth they reached Genoa it was to be met with grim news. An uprising of the populace had made Rome a howling confusion. Moreover, the armies of the rebels were gaining in the North and East. Hearing this, the Cardinals, who had been wanting only sufficient excuse, voted in consistory to return at once to Avignon.

Gregory had, of course, been struggling with himself as well as with the others. Now he felt himself awash in a tide he could not breast. His despair would have been complete, had he not known that one rope yet swung within the grasp of his sinking will. He had just learned that Catherine Benincasa was still in Genoa.

One evening Madonna Scotti summoned Neri and Fra Raimondo into the upstairs hall-way. "A priest is below asking to see Caterina," said she. "Will you admit him?"

Without preliminary inquiry, they agreed to do so and escorted the muffled figure into Catherine's room. Their knock was answered and as they entered the candle-lighted room, they saw her come forward wonderingly. Before Fra Raimondo could speak she fell with a gasp upon her knees.

"It is the Holy Father!" she cried.

Neri, in the act of swiftly and silently withdrawing, absorbed a picture he never forgot. In that little dim room the head of the Christian world stood motionless and bent upon Catherine's uplifted face a look of desperate supplication.

To himself the stupefied young man whispered, "She is his Conscience!"

Nothing was ever revealed about that interview. It went on until late into the night. But Gregory's Conscience was not sought in vain. Before many days the Papal party set sail for Livorno on the way to Rome.

Chapter Eight

Dearest Brother: This will tell you that the Friday following our departure we happily arrived in Siena; although our journey was not accomplished without some fears, for the road from Peccioli is uncertain and some awful things happened there. Had I foreseen them I would never have chosen that way and I warn you so you may be prudent. I am firmly convinced that the prayers of our sweet Mamma helped us greatly since all passed off so well.

I have given to Sano all the letters and the other things which you entrusted to me; then I distributed the other letters and did all the errands with which I was charged. The sons and daughters of our Mamma are rejoiced and await her as I do with extreme impatience. It seems to me she is much too slow. For if I find you staying too long I shall repent having come back and perhaps in that case I shall come myself to bring you a letter. I say no more except to give my love to the sweet Mamma and recommend me to my fathers—Brother Raimondo, Brother Master, Brother Felice; my love to Monna Lapa and salute for me my mothers—Monna Cecca, Monna Alessa, Monna Lisa and ask them to pray for me, wretch that I am. God knows what I should do if the thought that this separation will be short did not console me.

NERI finished reading this missive with a low laugh. It brought before him with peculiar vividness the boyish face of Stefano Maconi. How he had hated to go back to Siena at his mother's insistence and leave the *Bella Brigata* here in Pisa. It was amusing to reflect that nine months ago Stefano had hardly heard of these people and would have scorned them utterly, yet now could not exist without their society. Rolling up the parchment Neri thrust it into the pouch hanging from the belt of his tunic.

He had brought the letter with him to the Campo Santo to read as he paced the cloister. Often the young poet sought out the brooding melancholy of its beauty as a panacea for the problems and the personalities which filled his hours. Not only did streams of Pisan people pour in all day for interviews with Catherine, but now that Monna Lapa and Fra Tommaso della Fonte and six others had come from Siena to join the party there was no instant's peace.

Here, however, where his feet trod softly on the inscriptions over tombs sunk within the floor, here where he loved to linger before the famous fresco of the "Triumph of Death," he could reflect at leisure. A shaft of November sunlight etched against deep shadows the lattice work of stone above delicate pillars and turned the grass plot of the court into an emerald pool. How remote this lovely austerity from the hideous struggle of the world—the clash of armies, the sad journey of the Pope toward the turmoil of Rome! The little Mamma could sustain her marvellous pitch of activity because she had what she so often recommended to others— the power to shut herself into the "cell of self-knowledge" and "the knowledge of the goodness of God." But he himself still depended on some restoring external beauty.

At this point in his reflections the cathedral bell struck softly and Neri noticed that the sunshine was almost gone. Suddenly this place of death struck chill to his heart. Images of Catherine's loving greeting, of Monna Lapa's cheerful prattle and of the cosy supper table filled him with irresistible longing. Outside the gates, he paused for just an instant to watch the setting sun place an aureole about the summit of the leaning Campanile. Then at top speed he hurried home.

Stefano Maconi had time to send two more piteous appeals for the return of Catherine and her friends, before at last they started. On the eve of their departure Neri dispatched a letter from the Mantellata to the Pope. News had come that after awful storms at sea and even a shipwreck on the island of Elba, the Papal fleet had finally landed at Corneto and that Gregory would wait there until negotiations with Rome were successful. In the south Queen Giovanna of Naples was fighting without much success against his enemies. Catherine wrote to hearten him and implore him to make peace.

A powder of snow was on the streets, fur-lined mantles enfolded the burghers and the peal of bells rang brightly in the crisp December air when once again the *Brigata* came riding through the Porta Camoillia. It was nearly Christmas. To Stefano, Andrea Vanni, Matteo Cenni and a dozen others it seemed as if there had never been so glad a Christmas. The first reunion of the Fellowship was a *festa* of pure joy. There were thankful prayers and a lusty chorus of anthems. Later about a roaring fire on the hearth they exchanged all that personal news so dear to them. The story of Avignon was told and retold and discussion of world affairs was interlarded with bits of local gossip.

"Dearest Mamma," said Andrea Vanni when there came a lull in the talk, "what didst thou think when the government dealt so harshly with thy regenerated black sheep? After Nanni di Ser Vanni lost his fortune and was clapped into prison for his debts, we did all suppose he would repent his change of heart."

Fra Raimondo nodded, "*Si*, it seemed a strange recompense for conversion."

Catherine answered swiftly. "Not so. Before he drew toward Goodness he was of the world and the world loved him. Now that he hath turned his back upon it, it takes revenge. Misfortune is part of his soul's growth and he knows it well or otherwise he would not have made so excellent a gift to God through me."

"What gift was that, daughter? Thou tellest me nothing," grumbled Monna Lapa.

It was Maco di Sano, the merchant, who replied. "Nanni di Ser Vanni did bestow upon Caterina his castle of Belcaro. Truly, a princely gift."

"Belcaro?" gasped old Lapa, clapping her fat hands together. "*Dio mio!* It is the finest site near our city. Ser Vanni gave it to thee, my Caterina? Hardly can I believe in such riches. Perchance now the proud folk who think so ill of thee will know thee a person of consequence—above all when we set out in the heat of summer for our great *castello* on the hill. Ungrateful girl, never to tell your poor mother of this magnificent possession!"

Catherine joined merrily in the laughter aroused by her mother's indignation. "Possession of mine it is not. At Belcaro I shall found a retreat for Tertiaries of the Order of San Domenico. Thou shalt go there, my mother, but rather to worship God than to escape the city's heat."

Eagerly Matteo Cenni asked, "Hast thou a disposition from the Holy Father to found this retreat?"

As Catherine replied in the affirmative a memory of Gregory's gracious manner of granting this authority brought the image of him vividly before her. It always inspired in her heart a dual feeling—human pity for the stormy fate of a truly gentle being and a kind of divine rage at his weakness and the worldliness of his point of view.

Meanwhile Cristofano di Gano Guidini had remarked with his important air, "Now we await the consent of the Signoria for this transaction and it will soon be forthcoming, rest assured."

The talk swept on. Catherine heard Father Tantucci speak of William Flete, the Bachelor, and of the holy meditations he had set down in writing. That picture of the contented hermit brought up by contrast the image of a man at war with himself and suddenly the question she had suppressed all evening rose to her lips. Her mournful eyes searched the circle of happy faces and she spoke in a tone of poignant longing.

"And what of my dear son? Why is he not with us? None of you have so much as uttered his name. Tell me, where is Francesco Malavolti?"

There fell a grieving silence. Those who had remained in Siena knew all too well the reversion to his former life made by the handsome scapegrace. Matteo Cenni said sternly, "He is unworthy to call thee Mamma and he feels so and keeps away."

Catherine leaned forward in her chair, "You must on no pretext judge either the acts or the motives of others, Matteo. In our fellow creatures only the will of God should be considered." Suddenly the sternness in her face changed to angelic sweetness. "Tomorrow, Stefano, do thou go to the Malavolti palace and tell my son I wish to receive him at once. The Birthday of Our Lord is a time only for forgiveness of sin."

Gladly Stefano promised. But, though he went and saw Francesco for a moment, the latter would not give his word to accept that loving invitation. Later Neri tried to lure the back-slider with a special message direct from Fonte Branda. But the young man remained glum and distant with his friend. At last Catherine wrote him a note.

Dearest and more than dearest: I, a wretched mother, go about seeking and sending for you. Alas, where are now your noble desires? Comfort my soul and do not be so cruel to your own salvation in making your visits so rare. Break this knot; come, come, dearest son. I may well call you dear; you are costing me so much in tears and sweat and much bitterness. . . . If you but come and remain I ask nothing more except that you do the will of God.

This message proved irresistible and when Francesco knelt before her, Catherine greeted him with a warmth untinged by reproach. The young man was the more touched by her concern because he had never known her more occupied. Important letters came to her daily from the four corners of Italy and one long expected, brought toward the middle of January, announced glorious news from Rome.

There antagonistic civil factions had submitted to the proposals sent from Corneto and on the thirteenth the Pope and his retinue entered the Eternal City. It was a mighty processional through streets redeemed from melancholy. Before Gregory's white mule the Romans cast olive branches and shouted in delirium of joy. Those who were not in the street gathered on roofs and balconies to pelt the august figure with blossoms and confetti. A thousand lamps were lighted on Saint Peter's square and by every means the vacillating folk assured their

Prince that, for the time at least, their hearts were his.

Many of the dignitaries in that assembly knew full well who was responsible for this long-heralded return. Matteo di Giovanni has painted the historic scene with Catherine Benincasa leading the triumphal way. But she was only there in spirit. Far away in her humble little room she knelt upon the tiles before the Crucifix and in isolated silence poured out her heart in gratitude. What more auspicious opening could there be for this year of 1377?

She wrote the Pope at once, of course. In this letter she courageously discussed the temporal power of the Church. Without denying the Papal right to govern and defend its possessions, she asserted that such duties weighed little against the saving of souls. Battles, she said, could never bring about God's kingdom so well as peace.

Before the end of January Catherine received from the Signoria legal title to Belcaro and sanction for her plan to make the fortress a convent for Tertiaries. The next month it was dedicated with great solemnity under the name of "Saint Mary of the Angels." A Papal representative, the Abbot of San Antimo, was present and the first Mass was celebrated by William Flete of Lecceto.

Toward evening, after the ceremonies, Neri, Francesco and Stefano climbed the ramparts to the watch tower for the view. The last named two had visited the castle often when Nanni di Ser Vanni owned it and had attended many a revel there. The contrast between the uplifting beauty of the dedication they had just witnessed and the wildness of those remembered scenes of gambling and carousal seemed to the young men some slight measure of Catherine's effect upon the world.

Neri, who had never seen this prospect before, leaned over the massive wall in delight. Below was a thicket of scrub oaks defending the steep hill like a second rampart. Straight across the undulating country, startlingly close in the clear, bright air, stood Siena. Its red roofs were piled like overlapping shells at the feet of the Duomo. Rising delicate as foam and strong as ivory, its great white silhouette dominated the foreground. Behind it and to left and right perpendicular shafts of stone shot upward beside the palaces to make a frowning frame for that tall red lily with its creamy top, the bell-tower of the Signoria.

"*Bella città!*" murmured Stefano dreamily.

"Yes," said Francesco, "if cities have a soul Siena must possess one."

Turning swiftly at that, Neri looked down into the courtyard where with the hermit of Lecceto a slight figure in white and black was walking to and fro. "*Ecco!*" he whispered. "The soul of Siena is she."

When April came these comrades and all the Fellowship were glad that Catherine was at Belcaro. The songs of tomtit and thrush, the sweetness of periwinkles and violets must, they thought, do something to deaden the bolt of horror which then came hurtling from the north.

All who had striven for the Church felt themselves bathed in blood and shaken with anguish. A catastrophe had happened at Cesena, a town belonging to the League. It had been besieged by John Hawkwood, the English captain, who was still a hireling of the Papal forces. When he attacked and conquered it, he proceeded in cold blood to execute and murder every person in it—all the defenders and allies. Houses burned, palaces razed to the ground, beautiful works of art destroyed and the streets paved with four thousand corpses—such was the monument the mercenaries left to the need of defending the possessions of the Church. All Italy seethed with bitterness and terror.

When Catherine wrote to Gregory Eleventh after this tragic crime, her words had the sound of heart-broken sobs.

Oh, very Holy Father, I abjure you by the love that you have for Christ Crucified to follow in his steps. . . . *Oimè! Oimè!* Peace, peace, for the love of God, peace! . . . *Oimè, Oimè, Babbo mio,* curses on my miserable soul which by its sins causes all evil to arise! It seems that the demon has become master of the world!

Yet she made not a single direct reference to this monstrous crime committed in the name of the Church.

As Neri wrote down that letter he marvelled at the restraint of such an omission on the part of one who so deeply loved all Italy. But he was troubled about the frozen suppression of Catherine's grief and it seemed to him perilous to her sanity—especially since Fra Raimondo was absent just then —that no great demand was made upon her ener-

CATHERINE SET OUT ALONE DOWN THE FAMILIAR STREETS

gies. He soon learned, however, that the genius of this woman was destined never to be idle. Hardly had she returned from Belcaro when there occurred one of the most dramatic incidents in her career.

She found Siena in an uproar. It concerned a young nobleman from Perugia, Niccolò Toldi, who stood on the very brink of what was then considered eternal damnation. Condemned to death, he refused to confess his sins and receive the Eucharist.

"Only for a slight discourtesy to the Magnificent Lords of our Signoria, little Mamma," raged Francesco Malavolti, "this Toldi has been sentenced to die. Powerful men have besought mercy for him and two Cardinals at Rome wrote to demand his pardon. All in vain. Tomorrow he will go to the scaffold."

"So great is his bitterness," declared Andrea Vanni, "that he denies God altogether and will not see a priest."

Urged by the Dominicans and all her friends to visit this unfortunate youth in prison, Catherine set out alone down the familiar streets. The ruthless injustice of that sentence was like a weight upon her mind. But what gave her greater anguish was the possibility that the Signoria's victim would die unaware of the love of God. She entered his dungeon with the prayer that she might bring him knowledge. But hardly had the keeper turned the lock and left her in that gloomy place when the prisoner, recognizing her Dominican costume, burst into a wild volley of curses. With his bloodshot eyes, tumbled hair and the rumpled garments that had once been handsome, Niccolò Toldi was a terrifying figure.

But neither through sight nor hearing was Catherine in the least affected. She stood quite still in the dim light and without wasting a fragment of force upon human pity, so concentrated her entire being upon Divine love that it flowed from her like a magnetic current. Suddenly, as if he were swept by it beyond himself, the young man ceased to rave. She spoke then and he listened. In that mighty cosmic picture of the Spiritual World the enormity of his own doom began to dwindle and Reality flooded his consciousness. This was Truth! To know it was not to have lived in vain! Death seemed all at once a gateway to experience and his terror and resentment vanished.

Flinging himself on his knees and lifting a face completely transformed, the young man begged his heavenly visitant to talk further. And when, at last, the guard came to say gruffly that the time was up, Toldi promised to receive a priest for the confessional and implored Catherine to come again next morning. He must see her, he said, once more before he went to his execution.

That next day's meeting was described by Catherine to Father Raimondo in the most celebrated of her letters.

Then in the morning before the bell tolled I went to him and he was very glad. I took him to hear Mass and he received the Holy Communion which he was never to receive again. His will was attuned and subjected to the will of God and there alone remained a fear of not being brave at the last moment.

But the boundless and flaming goodness of God surpassed his expectation, inspiring him with such great love and desire of God that he could not remain without Him and he said to me, "Stay with me and do not leave me. And so I cannot be other than well; and I die content." And he laid his head upon my breast.

After she had consoled him, Catherine promised to wait for him at the place of execution. At this, clasping her hands in his, young Toldi cried, "I shall go there all joyous and strong and it will seem a thousand years to me before I reach it, when I think that you are waiting for me there."

Up the steps of the scaffold to the booming of the grim bell, went the little figure in its worn black mantle. Below in the square, impelled not only by the usual morbidness of crowds, but by the amazing story of Toldi's swift conversion, hundreds of people stood watching. Catherine, however, saw only one person, the advancing prisoner. His eyes were alight. Eagerly his pale lips whispered to her to make the sign of the Cross. This she did, knelt with him beside the block and, as the doomed youth meekly stretched out his neck for the headsman, her hands curved about to support his head.

At this a gasp went through the crowd. Men looked at that woman's face, tender and exalted, and could not believe she would have the courage to remain there during the awful moment when the axe descended. How could they know she had exchanged the temporary horrors of the present for a realm which would receive all that was immortal of Niccolò Toldi? When the awe-struck spectators saw an unfathomable look of joy shining from those two young faces, they crossed themselves in silence.

As the blow fell, no shadow subdued the glow of pure love in Catherine's face. She lifted her eyes as if she were following that departed spirit's flight. Only then did a cloud pass over that wonderful expression and it did so because, as she said in the concluding sentence of her letter, "I remained on earth with the greatest envy."

This unparalleled example of heroic effort for a soul in extremity raised the name of Catherine Benincasa to a new level in the hearts of her townsfolk. Not that there were wanting many who shrank in horror from this deed. These were the ones who disapproved of her for travelling about so much and for keeping open house for a fantastic group of followers. Such persons knew a woman's rightful place and were certain it offered no such freedom or scope of action.

Yet even among the most conservative were individuals who saw Catherine as she was. Strangely enough in this latter number were members of the most powerful and celebrated house of Siena—the Salimbeni. It was a family always at war. Once by that famous intrigue with Emperor Charles Fourth, the head of the Salimbeni had plunged the entire city into battle. More recently one of them became an outlaw and harassed the town as if he had been a foreign desperado. Now in this spring of 1377 between the two branches of the house had arisen so violent a quarrel that its ramifications threatened the peace of the community.

When, therefore, the contestants turned to Catherine with a request to arbitrate their dispute, the other nobles and the commune heaved a great sigh of relief. They thought it a stroke of marvellous good fortune that the Mantellata was in the city to re-establish concord. As soon as delle Vigne returned, he strongly recommended that Catherine undertake this service and, although she knew it would be an uncertain and thankless task, she rejoiced to check the smallest outbreak of the turbulence which made the world so hideous. The mission took her down into the precipitous Val d'Orcia where each party to the quarrel possessed a castle and with her went nearly twenty of the Fellowship.

On the way they stopped at Montepulciano where most of them had friends. Neri loved the sleepy town with its steep cobbled streets and the brilliance of its sudden vistas framed between brown walls and arches—vistas of sunny country and olive orchards stretching away to purple hills. A nobleman and poet whom he knew there was presented by him to Catherine and that encounter was long afterward celebrated in stanzas of rapturous praise penned by the poet in her honour. When the time came to leave, Cecca, who had a daughter in the convent, decided to linger in the old hill town and Monna Lapa kept her company. But all the rest went on into the wild, desolate region where the people were untamed as the landscape.

The Salimbeni quarrel proved a difficult and

tedious knot to untie. At the first castle it required weeks of conference before even a basis of agreement had been achieved. Then, while Alessa and Cecca went off to persuade one of the sisters, the remainder of the *Brigata* progressed to the Rocca d'Orcia to settle the final terms.

Val d'Orcia had a reputation for ferocity and utter indifference to religion. Yet news of Catherine's coming had been carried—secretly, mysterously—from the depths of tangled hollows to the loftiest crags where lonely huts of shepherds huddled perilously. Up from the valleys, winding down from the mountains, sometimes a hundred in a single day, these people came to find her—peasants, brigands, families of independent lords. Some brought with them ailing members of their households—the sick, the degenerate, the crazy. They filled the castle courtyard every day and seven priests were kept busy hearing confessions and administering Communion.

One morning when Neri, ensconced upon a stone bench near the fortress wall, was watching this strange and touching procession, he was joined by Francesco Malavolti. The latter, with an inclusive gesture of his arm, said, "Wouldst thou not think that such a mighty harvest for the Lord—even though much of this human grain is mildewed, rotten and unworthy—might be comprehended as a vast work of love, important to be done?"

Smiling, Neri nodded. It was a pleasure to have Francesco back with them again to deliver his pungent comment. "Who doth believe otherwise?"

The other tapped his pouch. "I have a letter here just dictated by our dearest Mamma to allay suspicion among the Lords of Siena. Ever must she explain to people why she lingers here. First it is to our grandmother Lapa, weary of convent life in Montepulciano. Next it is to friends at home who bewail her absence. Now it is to the Signoria. Those animals fear plots are hatched at the Rocca." He pulled down his mouth in disgust.

"I know," replied Neri, his face clouding. "The governors have sent a message to recall our Mamma from her labours. It is an outrage. Yet remember that the Salimbeni are feared and hated and plots do simmer in their heads and have before this boiled over on the city. The Lords know not what goes on down here and many are the men who will go to them and decry the little Mamma, saying she loves intrigue."

Catherine knew this quite as well as her secretaries. That letter dispatched by Francesco clearly reveals the indignant hurt of finding people so petty.

Dearest Brothers and Lords! . . . You know that a long time ago you began to negotiate this peace, but it was never concluded. Therefore, I should not wish it to be left again through my carelessness or through going away at once; because I should be afraid of being reproved by God. I shall conclude it as soon as I can, according as God gives me grace. . . .

I am sorry for the toil and fatigue my citizens are going to in thinking and talking about me. It seems they have nothing else to do but throw missiles at me and at my

company. They are right about me, because I am full of
defects; not so the others. But we, through enduring,
shall win; because patience is never conquered, but is always the victor.

Despite this explanation, however, new accusa-
tions and new demands for her return forced her
to write a second time to the Sienese governors and
say firmly, "I will go or shall stay according as the
Holy Spirit directs."

In the face of real problems such interfering
criticism was but the buzzing of flies. The Pope,
for example, seemed now quite as much an enemy
to peace as did the rebels themselves. He had neither
uttered any propitiatory censure of the atrocities at
Cesena nor yielded one jot or tittle of his claims
against Florence. Moreover, an embassy sent to
Rome from Siena just then gained little or nothing
in the way of conciliation. Catherine was the more
stung by the latter failure because she had forwarded to Gregory a special recommendation for
her fellow citizens and had said, "If there are any
people in the world who can be taken with love, it
is these."

Yet, despite her oneness with the city of her
birth, it was Italy—the whole of it—over which she
yearned. That Milan, Venice, Naples, Tuscany
should be at peace, that there should be union between these Christians of one blood and one language was her dominating passion. It set her apart
in greatness of conception from anyone of her
time. Indeed, so far-flung into the future was her
impulse that by five hundred years it preceded

realization. Not until the Risorgimento in the middle of the nineteenth century was Italy at last made one nation.

That these ideas should be placed once more before the Head of the Church, Catherine now sent Father delle Vigne to Rome. Her political prospectus included Papal appointments of peace-loving and intelligent prelates in place of French tyrants, generosity in negotiations with rebellious cities and continued activity for the Crusade. It was a sagacious plan. But from the Vatican was wafted back to her only a sense of loss and defeat.

Francesco and Neri were both with her on the terrace when Catherine received a letter announcing the first of her cruel disappointments. It appeared that shortly after Fra Raimondo's arrival in the Papal City he had been appointed Prior of the Church of Santa Maria sopra Minerva by the Master of his Order. That meant that he would remain in Rome and would return no more to be Catherine's close counsellor and guide.

"It is hardly a thing to be believed!" cried Francesco. "The Holy Father himself nominated Frate Raimondo to be thy confessor and now thou art deprived of him!"

For an instant Catherine could but close her eyes in an anguish of realization. At last she said in a shaken voice, "Truly I yet have for my Confessors Fra Bartolommeo and Fra Tommaso and I am blessed in my dear sons and daughters. But, *oimè*, I have none now to whom to give vent!"

"For Father Raimondo it is, also, sad, little Mamma," murmured Neri.

That she well believed. She recognized that it must have hurt delle Vigne to the quick when, a few weeks later, he was obliged to write that her suggestions had been coldly received and that Gregory seemed antagonistic to her. The information gave her an increased sense of isolation. No longer daring to write directly to the Vatican, she sent her *Babbo* a wild appeal in a letter to Raimondo. "To whom shall I turn if you abandon me?" she cried. But still Gregory manifested no sign of response. The rebuff was all the more cutting because she felt she might have been of use in the Florentine situation. Their defiance of the Pontiff had now reached the point where the city paid no attention to his interdict and was forcing the priests to hold church services. Contempt of Papal authority could go no further.

As the chill October winds swept over Val d'Orcia and most of the *Brigata* returned to Siena, Catherine felt herself at the very nadir of frustration. Moreover, her health and strength had never been at lower ebb. Yet those who remained with her saw little sign of this personal despair. She made visits to all the convents and monasteries in the neighbourhood and completed with vigour the details of the Salimbeni reconciliation. As if for reward of such heroic drudgery she received a sudden, magic dispensation. She learned to write!

In a distant room of the castle she was discovered one day bending over a table with a look of rapt absorption. With a quill dipped in a little pot of red ink, she was tracing upon a parchment in clear letters a prayer composed in verse. Upon her observer Catherine turned a radiant face. "*Ecco!* I, too, can use the pen. I shall write a letter myself to Father Raimondo." And during the next weeks she plied her new skill with unbounded satisfaction.

Unfortunately, when delle Vigne received this almost miraculous missive, he was in no mood to appreciate it. At close hand Gregory's situation appeared awful. There was in all Italy but one Papal supporter—the notorious Giovanna of Naples; all ambassadorial missions had failed; John Hawkwood with his mercenaries had now gone over from the Church to the League and was winning victories against the Pontifical forces. It was a moment fraught with grave peril. Out of it, however, came an opportunity which changed the face of the world for Catherine.

It seemed that one Sunday morning as Fra Raimondo descended from his pulpit at sopra Minerva, he was requested to go at once to see the Pope. The latter told him he had received a message that if Catherine of Siena would betake herself to Florence peace would be immediately concluded. When delle Vigne protested that he and others would gladly submit to martyrdom for the Vicar of Christ, Gregory said: "I do not wish you to go to Florence. They would maltreat you, but I believe they would not dare attack Caterina, both because she is a woman and because they venerate her." He then commanded Raimondo to be there next day with the bulls and other papers necessary for Catherine's official mission.

Such was the news, backed up by proper documents, which reached the Rocca one December day. The family had been gathered about the fire while Catherine read from the Breviary, but the arrival of this letter had charged the air with glad excitement. Catherine's face was all joyous anticipation and the dark old room buzzed with talk, laughter, the immense relief of significant activity.

When at last she had escaped into her own room, however, Catherine's gratitude soared upward in a solemn pæan of thanksgiving. No longer was she an outcast from grace. The Vicar of Christ had chosen her of all his children to take up this important task. Oh, glorious opportunity to spend herself for Italy and peace!

Once more the Fellowship reunited in Siena for the Christmas celebration. But it was only to say good-bye. For less than a fortnight later Catherine set out for Florence. This time her companions were but five—Alessa, Cecca and another Mantellata, Neri and Stefano.

Those fortunate young men were given a solemn warning by Francesco Malavolti. "This is no ordinary journey," said he. "Dangers await you all in that city of strife. *Dio mio*, I would I were also going! But guard well our little Mamma!"

Neri, pressing his friend's hand, replied with gentle irony: "Who can guard the falcon in its upward flight? But fear not. Danger is less sure than disappointment, for I trust little in the Florentine talk of peace and have no security even in Messer Niccolò Soderini at whose palace we stay as before."

As a matter of fact Soderini had instigated this visit. While Catherine was at the Rocca he had come to Siena for a conference with Fra Raimondo before the latter set out for Rome. As a leader of the Guelfs and member of the Florentine government, his plan for peace carried weight and Catherine felt there was every hope of victory. It was a glorious beginning for the new year of 1378.

After the long, cold, wearisome ride the travellers were glad enough to assemble in the great *sala* of the Soderini palace about the festal board. When the repast was over and all were gathered about the roaring fire which made more brilliant the rich designs painted on the heavy oak beams, Catherine came down from her room and joined the company. A dozen Florentine friends were there to welcome her and among them that lovely youth, Barduccio Canigiani.

"Wilt thou now accept me for a son, also?" he immediately implored. And when she did so with a smile of tender welcome, he rushed over to Neri and Stefano to receive from them the dear name of brother.

That loving concern for her which the Canigiani family always manifested now had a most practical demonstration. The elder brother, who was one of the captains of the Guelfs, collected sufficient funds to build for Catherine a little house on a steep street set back from the left bank of the river, the Costa San Giorgio. There Catherine and her five companions were established in complete independence and comfort. Meanwhile the youngest boy, Barduccio, had joined the staff of secretaries and became an enthusiastic member of the family.

When he and his fellow scribes had time, he escorted them to all the cathedrals of the town and on pilgrimages about the Tuscan hills. Neri long remembered the day they spent at Fiesole. Those ruins of the ancient theatre there gave him the key to that romantic feeling for Rome so vividly expressed by Petrarch.

As he looked down into the grass-grown amphitheatre and imagined how audience and spectacle must once have looked, the young man had a sudden vision of all the treasured memories stored in the Eternal City. Smiling at the others he quoted softly, "The ancient walls which yet make the world fear and love and tremble, with memories of time gone-by ———"

"*Sì, sì,*" cried Barduccio delightedly, "that poem of classic beauty!"

Stefano looked at them indulgently. He did not read poetry and he wondered when the February sun shone so warm and the sky was so blue why these two needed any comment of man to increase their satisfaction. As he turned away, he thought with a pang how all three of them with their male strength were here revelling in beauty while back in the city, in one of the council chambers of the Palazzo Vecchio, the fragile Catherine was following tedious sessions of the Guelfs. They were wily, worldly men she had to guide toward constructive action for peace.

Abruptly he interrupted the happy colloquy of the two scholars. "Barduccio, does thy brother say if the Florentines are pleased with what takes place at the Holy Father's peace conference at Sarzana?"

The others blinked up at him from the antique stone bench upon which they were seated in the sun. Neri had an impulse to cry out that they had come for a little rest from politics and problems, but his companion's quick response to the intensity of Stefano's face checked his protest. Moreover, as the others talked, his poetic imagination leaped back from contemplation of the past and endowed the present with something of that same glow.

Were they weaving history now, he wondered, even as in the days when Augustus trod the streets of Rome? That plan of Gregory's might prove the woof of a new fabric for the world. In January the Pope had persuaded all parties—the Roman Curia, France, Venice, Naples and the League—to send representatives to the congress at Sarzana. Bernabo Visconti of Milan had consented to preside and already word had come that agreement was certain on one point, at least. This was the amount of indemnity the rebels were to pay the Church. It was a felicitous beginning. If only here in Florence the local factions could be reconciled!

All the way back to the city, the three secretaries argued the possibilities of civic peace. But they did not quite grasp the situation. Neither did Catherine, at first. With the narrow selfishness perennially characteristic of party organizations, but intensified by the ferocity of the age, the Guelfs were using their power chiefly to revenge themselves on private enemies.

Moreover, they did not play fair with their high-minded counsellor from Siena. By dint of telling her merely that certain troublemakers should leave the city, they won her agreement for a policy of banishment which they proceeded to use wholesale. As soon as she realized what the Guelfs were doing, Catherine protested with all her force. But in vain! Neither consideration of public good, nor the purpose for which they had summoned her checked these men from indulging in the sweet delight of ousting the men the did not like.

What the Mantellata did accomplish, however, was to persuade Florence to obey the Papal interdict. The services held in its defiance were abandoned. Anent this renewed obedience, she wrote to William Flete.

It seems to me that the first light of dawn begins to show and that our Saviour has enlightened these people in order to lessen that lamentable blindness into which they fell in celebrating by force the holy mysteries.

Between that change for the better and the encouraging aspect of the general peace conference Catherine's hopes of success rose high during March. Moreover, she had the supreme happiness of receiving a cordial letter from the Pope. Each day she would say to herself that if it only might be permitted her to lay the olive branch at the feet of "her sweet *Babbo*," she would be blessed beyond earthly recompense.

Once more, however, the cup of fulfilment was to be dashed from her hand. Late in March came a day when all the bells began to toll, when heralds passed from street to street crying tidings of woe and people gathered mournfully outside the closed churches. Within the little house on the Costa San Giorgio the family gathered to discuss how they would break the news to Catherine. She was closeted in meditation, but the commotion roused her and she hurried down the stairway.

"What is it? What has happened?"

Barduccio Canigiani alone had the courage to tell her. Flinging himself upon his knees, he said solemnly, "His Holiness Gregory Eleventh is dead!"

Gregory dead, a new Pope to be elected! Catherine stood dazed. An instant afterwards it swept over her what that meant—the dispersal of the conference just on the verge of peace, the overturning of every policy, the frustration of all effort, perhaps even another French Pope chosen and a consequent return of the Curia to Avignon! Oh, inexplicable stroke of bitter destiny!

Suddenly then she sank upon her knees and said gently, "My children, we must pray for the departed soul of our Holy Father."

Before the day was over Catherine held a conference with her staff. Neri, supposing their mission at an end until the future was clear, asked her when they would start back to Siena. She lifted her head and said in a ringing tone, "Not until the city has become reconciled with Holy Church! For this purpose we came and not until it is accomplished shall we leave!"

On April eighth the election of the new Pope was held. The first messenger to Florence reported that Cardinal Tebaldeschi, a Roman, had been chosen. But immediately afterwards came another herald to deny the first report and offer full substantiation of the fact that not Tebaldeschi, but Bartolommeo Prignano, the Archbishop of Bari, was the new Pontiff who had taken the title of Urban Sixth. It was most confusing. But such a choice lifted a great weight from Catherine's heart. Prignano was an Italian and would keep the Holy See at Rome. Moreover, having met and talked with him in Avignon, she knew he was an upright man with high ideals of reform.

"I have but one fear," she said to the family the night they learned the facts. "The Holy Father may prove a man too quick of action, too little given to sympathy and understanding. With all the French Cardinals to win over, he should proceed with gentle pace—albeit with a firm tread."

"But what thinkest thou, little Mamma, did truly take place in Rome?" asked Alessa Saracini wonderingly. "Why did we receive that false report?"

When they finally heard the tale it was with foreboding. Incredible scenes had taken place in Rome. The unruly mob, fearing the action of foreign cardinals, had surged about the Vatican, roaring, "We want a Roman! A Roman!" It was enough to terrify the College—especially after the men had broken into the cellars of the palace and poured its fine wines down their throats! Insufficiently protected by guards, the Cardinals feared to confess the choice agreed upon. For Prignano was a Neapolitan, not a Roman. When, therefore, the wild-eyed crowd came rushing through the Vatican and climbing on the balconies, the prelates flung the Papal insignia over the protesting old Tebaldeschi and told the people he was Pope. Satisfied, the mob retired. And when next day they learned of the deceit, they tolerated it because, after all, no foreigner had been made Vicar of the Church.

Assuring Urban Sixth that his election had been valid, the Cardinals robed him in his splendid vestments, presented him to all the clergy and the people and nine days afterward in august ceremony crowned him before Saint Peter's. Immediately, through Catherine Benincasa's influence, the Florentines sent ambassadors to the new Pontiff. She herself had Fra Raimondo as a personal representative at the Vatican and learned that he had been well received there.

Thus in comparative calm and optimism passed May and most of June. Yet Florence was uneasy and for all the preventive efforts of the Mantellata the Guelfs continued in their policy of banishing all who encroached upon their precious power. Catherine's family were the more disturbed because her name had been linked with this dangerous injustice. On all sides they heard angry murmurs of discontent. At last, on the twenty-second of June the suppressed fury against the Guelf governors broke out. Their enemies had stirred up the mob and it rose with violence.

It was Barduccio Canigiani who came rushing early in the day with the news. "Thou must fly, sweetest Mamma, and thy sons and daughters with thee!" he shouted. "The people are mad with rage and curse thy name with ours. Already they rush through the streets and enter houses to spread terror."

Seated in a wooden arm-chair, Catherine looked up calmly from the Missal she was reading. "Let them come," she answered. "I shall not stir from here."

Stefano and Alessa, who had been down to the river to see whatever they could, returned shortly with fear in their eyes. "Plunder and fire are spreading everywhere. Thy house, Barduccio, is in flames and likewise that of Messer Soderini! They say the mob is breaking into the prisons to set everyone free to help in the destruction."

From afar the sound of shouting came up faintly. An echo of it was tossed from the little square of Santa Felicità nearby. "Down with the hypocrites! Down with Soderini and Caterina!"

Quietly the woman they vilified rose from her seat and went into the garden. The others followed her and sat down uneasily to wait. Over the high wall where yellow roses climbed, they could hear cries and sounds of running feet and the air was filled with the smoke drifting from burning palaces. Hours passed thus and then all at once the tumult became deafening. They heard the mob rushing up their very street and to their house. At the back of the garden the little group stood tense. Suddenly the gates burst open and the rabble was upon them.

Forward, straight toward them, sprang a slender figure and a clear voice rang out: "I am here! I am Caterina whom you seek. Take me and leave the others!"

With arms spread out, defenceless, and a smile of radiant welcome, she stood facing the wild, dishevelled men as they tumbled into the garden. Sticks and torches, spears and swords they bore and their bloodshot eyes fixed her in hatred. Yet they could come no nearer. The leaders wavered in confusion. That small person in her attitude of readiness, the silent, motionless figures there behind her —no, they could move no further, nor could a hand be raised to strike! Suddenly the invaders turned and ran.

Behind her Catherine heard a burst of laughter. Relief from tension and a sense of that high comedy broke into mirth from all the group. She, however, sank upon her knees and shook with bitter scbs.

The others rushed to her, crying, "Little Mamma, why dost thou weep when all the danger is over?"

She could not then explain her emotion, but she did so later in a letter to Raimondo da Capua.

But my desire to give my life for the Truth and the sweet Bride of Christ was not fulfilled. But the Eternal Bridegroom played a great joke on me. So I have reason to weep, because the multitude of my iniquities was so great that I did not deserve that my blood should give life or illumine darkened minds, or reconcile the sons with the father, or cement a stone in the mystical body of Holy Church.

This experience was typical of a destiny which permitted no desire to be wholly gratified. Nevertheless, although she grieved to be deprived of a martyr's death, she could rejoice at the "great mercy which I and my cherished sons and daughters have received." And she could be glad that before night had far advanced the Governors of Florence had the riot well under control. She was still considered to be in danger, however, and against her will was persuaded by the authorities to go to an hermitage outside the city until once more everything was normal within its walls.

To return from that retreat was to plunge in for a last effort to seal the peace. Catherine wrote an eloquent plea to Pope Urban Sixth and sent it through Fra Raimondo. The latter soon replied that the Holy Father was strongly disposed to end the war and to accept the Florentine terms. At this report the small house above the Arno was filled with the joy of approaching victory.

On July 18, 1378, that anticipated triumph was celebrated. At one o'clock in the afternoon from watch towers to the south a courier was descried on the road from Rome and swiftly the word was passed throughout the city. Housewives left their bread unbaked, weavers left their looms and everybody great and small rushed to the vast brown square before the Palazzo Publico. Catherine and her group hurried thither likewise. When they saw the Papal messenger spurring his horse forward and beheld what he carried in his hand tears of thanksgiving rained down their faces.

"Peace! Peace! Peace!" Hundreds of voices shouted the pæan. "The olive branch has come! It is the peace!" And all the bells of Florence in deep reverberation echoed the exultation of that cry.

In the courtyard of the Palazzo the messenger dismounted and gave the official letters which made the terms conclusive to the notary of the Republic. The olive branch was fastened at a window for all to see and from the balcony above the piazza the notary read the Pope's treaty to the crowd. Applause and shouts went up like thunder then and when darkness fell every sombre palace had flaming torches in the sconces and flares were lighted from the roofs of all the public buildings. People went singing and dancing through the streets and burned great bonfires beside the river. It was a city mad with joy.

True, the people had forgotten the woman who had gained for them this great victory. She, without whom no olive branch would have arrived from Rome, received no deputation of thanks, no word of gratitude. While excitement rocked the town Catherine sat alone with Neri in her little room. But she was not even conscious of neglect. All her being was one hymn of happiness and she was busy sending the glad tidings to Siena.

Oh, dearest children, rejoice, rejoice! The lame walk, the deaf hear, the blind see and the dumb speak, crying in a great voice, Peace, peace, peace!

Chapter Nine

"WHY is it that all the way from Florence our dearest Mamma hath not sung nor scarcely spoken? With our mission so well completed, why doth she still look sad?"

It was Cecca Gori who in a low tone asked the question—fat, middle-aged Cecca with her kind, wrinkled face. Leaning against the trunk of a tree, she sat in a circle with the others on the grass beside the road and her eyes anxiously searched the five faces.

The August day had just turned noon and already the travellers were more than half-way back to Siena. With the mules tied in the shade to rest, the party was eating a luncheon of bread, cheese and hard-boiled eggs. A perfect mound of black cherries and a bottle of wine, set in the midst of the circle, served to slake thirsty throats. At a little distance, under a pine tree sat Catherine. She had a book upon her knee, but her grave eyes were lifted to the pale azure sky.

Neri looked at Cecca with that expression of courteous patience which always veiled his boredom. "Hast thou forgotten, Monna Cecca, what happens now in Rome? With such reports of the Holy Father's disaffected Curia, our Mamma sees naught but a troubled future ahead."

"*Sì, sì*," chimed in Stefano, "when in consistory his Holiness doth say to Cardinal Robert of Geneva, 'Hold thy tongue!' and names another blockhead and yet another liar, it is plain that those haughty Cardinals we saw at Avignon will not bear such tempers long."

"It is impossible to believe Il Papa speaks thus," murmured Cecca.

Neri flung a look of eloquent impatience at Barduccio Canigiani. The boy had refused to leave Catherine and had quitted home and city to follow her and serve her cause. His fine dark eyes accepted Neri's appeal, but with no answering gleam of humour. Helping himself to a handful of cherries, he turned very earnestly to Cecca.

"Mother, dost thou not remember that one of our own family hath himself recently experienced this mad discourtesy from the Holy Father? When Fra Bartolommeo had an audience at the Vatican he was treated to a terrible burst of anger for small reason. Our little Mamma wrote at once to pacify our Father, but, also, to beg for a tiny bit of patience and kindness. He makes enemies of all with whom he has to deal."

Cecca sighed unhappily. "That I have heard. But he is a holy man who will not allow presents to be received by the clergy. Also he hath refused to let the French Cardinals go back to Avignon even for the summer and requires them to stay at Anagni. They say, too, he serves them with but one dish at meals."

An irrepressible laugh escaped from Neri's lips. Before his quick imagination flashed a picture of that dinner table—the thick-set, sallow Pope glowering at its head and on either side the disgruntled dignitaries.

In a tone of lively irony he said: "Truly, all such acts do help Urban Sixth's unruly tongue to please and soothe the Cardinals. We know they dearly love fasting and poverty and Italy in summer! Yet they strangely persist in displeasure. Fra Raimondo hath written us that no one is faithful to the Pope but that old Roman, Cardinal Tebaldeschi."

Stefano Maconi tugged at his leathern riding boots and then with thumb and finger flipped a cherry stone in the direction of a blackbird. "Had His Holiness but listened to our Mamma he would be in no such shackles. I did take down her letter beseeching him to create new Cardinals who would be holy men and eager for reforms. I remember her very words and they were these: '*Oimè! oimè!* Delay no longer; do not defer finding a remedy till the rock falls upon your head!'"

"Yes," agreed Alessa Saracini, rising and shaking

the crumbs from her mantle. "It is small wonder our Mamma wears a look of grief. She stares at coming ruin. I marvel she can ever be joyous and glad."

Pouring a few drops of wine into an earthen cup, Alessa walked over to Catherine and tenderly bent over her, "Drink this before we go forward in the heat, sweetest Mamma," she urged.

Catherine started slightly and then her sad face lighted with a lovely smile. "*Grazie, cara,*" she said, taking the cup, "would it were given me to serve the Bride of Christ as thou dost help and serve thy most unworthy friend."

She had been lost in profound reflection and all the way back home that afternoon, remained preoccupied. Neither the blazing sun nor the stings of gnats which so annoyed the others did she so much as feel. She was wondering whether these misfortunes befell the Holy Church to purge it of its ills. What could she do to serve better the Will of God in this matter? She felt that somehow she had failed.

Before she had been one week in Siena she was certain of it. To that city as to all cities and towns in Italy, to France and Germany and England, letters and messengers sped from Rome. They carried news which was to make history—news which to most Christians proved staggering beyond credibility. The great infallible Authority had been defied; as if he had been merely a senator the representative of Christ on Earth had been set at naught by a revolt of all the Cardinals. It was a human earthquake that shook the world.

Amid these reverberations of disaster, Catherine's words spoken three years before came back to members of the Fellowship. They remembered how at Pisa she had predicted that the clergy themselves would divide and revolt. They remembered also how she had spoken then as if she were a prophetess of stone, untouched by common tremors. Now, however, they saw her shaken by grief, protest, terrible self-blame.

Between them all they pieced out the details of catastrophe. It began when the French Cardinals were gathered all together at Anagni. Knowing three Italian members of the College to be neutral and the Pope at Tivoli, they had constructed a most finished plot against the Pontiff. Boldly they sent out a public statement that the election which had placed Prignano on the Papal throne had been made under duress and was illegal. That throne was, therefore, vacant and the Pope no pope at all. Promptly afterwards these rebels moved to Fondi under the protection of the Count of Fondi who had quarrelled with Urban Sixth. There—so they asserted—they would elect a true and legal Vicar of the Church.

When all these facts had been assembled at Catherine's conference, the group attempted courageously to look them in the face. Andrea Vanni pointed out one aspect of the situation. Said he: "Behind this audacity lurks the King of France. Charles Fifth ever wanted to dominate the Church and did dislike Urban from the start because he would not bend the knee."

Catherine said his words were wise, but urged that it might not yet be too late to stem the consequences of that flight to Fondi. Before she could so much as think out any plan, however, before the Fellowship could meet again, the revolt became complete. Suddenly at this crisis old Cardinal Tebaldeschi died and the three other Italian cardinals, after a period of wavering, set out for Fondi to join their colleagues. Urban Sixth was stark alone.

Yet not alone. Over mountains and valleys between herself and him Catherine Benincasa sped the might of her spirit to his aid. True, she shared his tortured horror, his fear, his utter bewilderment. No one so identified with the good of the Church as she could have escaped the most bitter distress. But, too virile to be crushed by it, she rose up magnificent and dauntless, to fight beside the Pope. With words of fire, she laid about his enemies and martialled his supporters.

She wrote to the Spanish Cardinal, Pedro de Luna, whom she had met in Avignon and bade him "be a man and a column which wavers not." To the Count of Fondi she sent a positive command that he withdraw his protection from the rebel Cardinals. Telling him that in his secret heart he knew the truth, she asserted that there could be but one legal Pope and he was Urban Sixth. She wrote the lonely Pontiff and mourned with him and begged him never to give up. For hours in the Capella delle

Volte at San Domenico she prayed that by her tears, her life, her every thought she might avert the cataclysm.

All in vain. One evening in late September just before the *cenacolo* Matteo Tolomei and Father Bartolommeo hurried into Catherine's house. Of those already gathered there the priest asked quickly, "Where is Caterina?"

Barduccio replied, "She hath gone with Alessa and Lisa on a pilgrimage to Santa Bonda to pray at the tomb of Giovanni Colombini."

Hardly had he finished speaking when a clear, gay voice on the stairway called out, "Are my children awaiting their wretched mother?"

The next instant, swift as a swallow Catherine was in the room. Her radiant smile circled the group. Then it vanished. Coming close to Father Bartolommeo, she said in a tone low, but so vibrant with apprehension that it was like a cry: "It has happened! News has come! Oh, my Father, tell me quickly what those demons have done."

Chokingly the priest answered: "The Antipope has been elected by the Cardinals at Fondi. It was done the twentieth of September."

A sound of mingled pain and fury swept the room. "Who is he?" cried everyone at once.

"He hath assumed the name of Clement Seventh. He is Cardinal Robert of Geneva."

In consternation they stared at one another. Then Francesco Malavolti howled: "That insensate animal? He who hath made such bloody war upon Italians? But two years ago with Bretons at his back he laid waste all the land about Bologna and there lives no one in Italy who hath forgotten the Cesena massacre—that he might have stopped!"

Catherine was a marble carving of despair. "Well have those hypocrites chosen their Antichrist!" she said bitterly. Slowly she turned her eyes from one to another and said: "Thus Christendom is split in half! Unless ———" her voice lifted and swelled, "by work, prayer and sacrifice we can yet prevent this evil from taking root!"

With her own words came a sense of relief. It was over—the horrible suspense. The very worst had happened and now the foe was named and in the open. Soon the universe would know who stood with the lovers of the Church and who were her enemies. Perhaps a sense of shame might still come to some of those traitors.

Within the week she had dispatched a scorching letter to the three Italian cardinals.

What shows me that you are ungrateful, coarse and mercenary? The persecution which you . . . inflict on that sweet Bride. . . . In spite of which you clearly know the truth that Pope Urban Sixth is truly Pope, the highest Pontiff, chosen in orderly election. . . . And so you announced it to us. Now you have turned your backs, like poor mean knights; your shadow has made you afraid.

What proves to me the regular election with which you chose Messer Bartolommeo, Archbishop of Bari, who today is made in truth Pope Urban Sixth? In the solemnity with which his coronation was observed this truth is clear to us. That the solemnity was carried out in good faith is shown by the reverence which you gave him and the favours you asked from him which you have used in all sorts of ways. You cannot deny this truth except with plain lies.

You could not endure, not only an actual correction, indeed, but even a harsh word of reproof made you lift up rebellious heads. . . . Before Christ on earth began to sting you, you confessed him and reverenced him as the Vicar of Christ that he is.

Speaking entirely in the natural sense—for according to virtue we ought all to be equal—speaking humanly, Christ on earth being an Italian, and you Italian, I see no reason but self-love why passion for your country could not move you. . . .

"Passion for your country!" Stefano Maconi repeated the words to himself after he had copied the letter. Before he knew Catherine Benincasa he had never conceived of such a thing. In his concentration on his family he had scarcely possessed a true love of Siena. But this woman suffered for all Italy and desired its good as most women desire the welfare of a favourite son. Dimly thus the disciple could gauge the depth of her desperation. She had brought back the Pope to Rome only that the Church might be sundered and Italy lose the vast prestige of having within her boundaries the sole and unique Pontiff of Christendom.

On the Sunday after that terrible news arrived many of the Fellowship, gathered at San Domenico, found themselves watching during Mass the face of their leader. Its mobile eloquence had taken on a different character from any aspect they knew. What was she thinking as she knelt there with that rapt expression—so sad, so passionate, and at the same time so glorified?

Neri whispered to Barduccio, "It is a creator's look."

The comment revealed the perception of the poet's mind. During Mass Catherine was absorbed in the composition of four prayers—for herself, for the Church, for peace between Christians, for the welfare of the earthly father of her soul, Raimondo da Capua. Faced by this vast tragedy of failure, she felt crystallizing within her the entire inner experience of her life. She was filled with an urge to express in some form the Truth as it had been revealed to her and give it to a bewildered and convulsed mankind.

In a long letter to delle Vigne she worked out a basis for her idea. Then she put the matter aside in order to write Pope Urban Sixth.

I have heard that those demons in human form have elected an Anti-christ against you. Now forward, most holy Father! Go into this battle without fear.

She then offered to go to him and serve in any way she could. On October fifth she sent off this message.

When Barduccio, who wrote it for her, said he had no doubt her presence would be immediately required in Rome, she would admit no certainty and merely said: "We shall see. If so, there is much to be done first."

One of the practical things she attended to was formally to arrange the administration of the Convent of Saint Mary of the Angels at Belcaro. For the most part, however, she passed her days in gathering up all the personal contacts she had developed at Siena within the ten years of her activity.

A peculiar solemnity characterized the meetings at the subterranean Church of the Madonna at La Scala. And when the circle gathered at the *cenacolo* the usual affectionate sympathy reached an almost unbearable pitch. It was as if they were taking leave of one another or of Catherine. Even the most prosaic member of the group felt that she was laying upon him a charge to work for the Truth however he could and as never before. This spirit of consecration—which was her very own—was the culmination of all the Fellowship had meant.

When she went out to visit the hermit at Lecceto a large group of friends accompanied her. Even William Flete was moved to lay aside his reticence and welcome her with an unwonted fulness of warmth. He plainly indicated that he realized this was an angelic visitation. Moreover, he seemed willing to bestir himself a little for the cause of the true Pope.

"Many letters have I written," said he to Catherine, "and shall write more for the enlightenment of everyone concerning Urban Sixth. And by God's grace my country of England will stand firm for him, come what may."

"Excellent, Brother William! Rest not nor cease to strive! This is the time for deeds." Catherine lifted her small face with its burning eyes to the peaceable friar and spread out her thin hands in an imperious gesture. Of the two she seemed far the more virile.

"Make known to me quickly what the Pope doth answer to your letter," said William Flete in a tone of mild interest. "He may need thee here rather than in Rome."

There was no denying that. Catherine had no choice but to hold all plans in abeyance until word came from the Vatican. But she did not wait with folded hands. In this interim she recognized her opportunity to set down the doctrine which was the result of her lifelong contemplation.

To obtain complete concentration free from duties and visitors, she slipped from the city and took refuge in one of those many retreats near Siena where, supported by the government, hermits enjoyed the meditative life. It was one of her close friends who offered her this shelter, Fra Santi da Teramo, formerly a disciple of Giovanni Colombini. Barduccio Canigiani, Neri and Stefano in turn acted as secretaries. On the ninth of October she began her dictation and on the thirteenth, she was once more in the midst of her circle in Siena. During those five days she had composed a book.

Il Dialogo, so called because it represented a conversation between the seeker for truth and the Giver of truth, became famous the length and breadth of Italy. The book was copied and recopied, treasured in the manuscript collections of great families, passed about for a century and when printing was introduced from Germany it was among the first works selected for the press. In Bologna Catherine's opus was printed during the year 1473.

While that dictation was still in progress Neri

walked out one shining noonday from town to the hermitage to relieve Barduccio's labours and Cristofano di Gano went with him. In the fields beside the rough path, peasants were gathering the olive crop and great baskets filled with the small dark globules stood here and there under the silvery foliage. Far to the south they could discern the peak of Monte Amiata and nearby the massive outlines of monasteries and castles rising above the forests.

Fra Santi's retreat consisted of a tiny house of brick and small, windowless chapel, marked only by a Cross. Pausing outside under the trees, Neri and Cristofano listened in silence. Through the open door and unshuttered window floated a voice, sweet, vibrating, unbroken even for a breath. The two men sat down upon the low wall of the garden and remained absorbed in what they heard.

"Already I have told thee," said the voice, "that the greater the love, the greater is the grief and pain, so that in whom grows love, grows grief. He who knows most, loves most and the more he loves the more he tastes of love. A person is of use to another creature to the extent that he loves him and no more, and he is wanting in service to the extent that he is wanting in love. From seeing himself loved he comes to love still more profoundly."

There was a long pause. Then, in quite another accent, the same voice said, "Barduccio, my son, thou must be weary. Thou hast been driving the pen for many hours. Why doth Neri delay to come to us?"

"We are here, sweetest Mamma," cried that young man and sprang quickly to the door.

As he entered he saw Barduccio raise his head from the parchment and, although the boy's face was drawn with fatigue, he said quickly, "I am not weary and could continue all day to set down these glorious thoughts."

Catherine had sent a smile of greeting to the newcomers. But now her eyes closed and, without further awareness of her surroundings, she began to walk up and down the narrow space. "Love begets love and love makes thee persevere ——" she said in the clear, breathless tone of a moment ago.

Swiftly Neri gestured to Barduccio to rise. Seating himself at the oak table in his place, he seized the pen and took up that rapid, continuous dictation. Barduccio in silence passed out into the garden. He feared the genial notary would follow him out and try to chat. But that individual, who had shyly seated himself upon a wooden bench near the door, was transfixed by an impression which became the treasure of his life.

What he saw was a woman consumed before his eyes by a passion struggling for utterance. Often panting, often speaking with tears coursing down her wasted cheeks, she lifted a face, now convulsed with anguish over an unheeding world and now lighted by the joy of faith in divine mercy. In his *Memoires* Cristofano made this comment on the *Dialogo*:

Also that said servant of God did a notable thing. It was a book the size of a Missal. And this was made by her, lost of every faculty except speech, God speaking in her. She talked and one wrote down what she said— sometimes Barduccio, sometimes Stefano and again Neri. To hear this seems an incredible thing, but to those who were writing and listening it was not so and I am one of those.

The notary made one of the first copies of the book and then, "because he who knows grammar and is cultured does not willingly read things in the common tongue," he translated the work, a little at a time, into Latin. It was Stefano's translation, however, which was most circulated among the Orders of the Church. Although dictated without revision, the book falls naturally into six parts—the Introduction and five treatises on Discernment, Prayer, Tears, Divine Providence, and Obedience. With its spiritual wisdom, its ardent and often beautiful phrasing, this great composition has proved a source of inspiration to countless pilgrims on the upward path.

Catherine's followers, versed as they were in these great conceptions, were able to regard the utter madness of their world as an unreality they could and must deal with. The crowning of Clement Seventh on October thirty-first and his immediate creation of nine new Cardinals brought the Schism before Christendom in all its gaping dreadfulness. Two Popes issuing orders to the clergy and presiding over ecclesiastical affairs, two Curias to arbitrate and make laws, two sets of Cardinals to supervise Bishops and Archbishops! How could the practise of religion continue under divided authority? Who was to obey whom?

As far as Italy was concerned, there was only one unexpected disloyalty. It came as a shock to find that Naples did not support its fellow citizen, Prignano, now Urban Sixth, but, instead, turned definitely against him. No one was surprised, however, that Savoia, Piemont and the duchy of Montferrato followed the lead of France and gave allegiance to Clement. Bavaria, Luxembourg and Scotland did likewise. On the other hand, all the rest of Italy, England, Hungary, Flanders, Poland and the new German Emperor, Wenceslas, gradually ranged themselves on the side of Urban Sixth. The latter held Rome, but only amid such uprisings as made the Vatican untenable and forced him to reside far down the river in the Trastevere. It was into this turmoil that Catherine Benincasa was now invited. The Pope's letter arrived and stated with great positiveness that he needed her in Rome.

Tidings of this summons went swiftly to all parts of Siena. That some of the winds which carried the news were contrary and blew on ready disapproval was first discovered by the four young men who had served so long as Catherine's secretaries. They had gathered one evening for supper at the house of Nanni di Ser Vanni, welcoming the invitation as a means of encouraging the former scapegrace in his new associations. During the meal they had talked to him mainly of a subject which filled their hearts —the marvellous book so recently completed.

After they had regained the *sala*, however, where

logs blazed on the hearth, the host brought up a cosier theme. "Since my late fall of fortune," said he genially, "I have sold most of my possessions and truly in this little house I was obliged to hire there is no room for many. Yet I should like to have you see one treasure I have kept."

Striding over to a carved chest with hasps of fine bronze-work, he drew from it a book bound in tooled leather, soft as a lady's cheek and embossed in gold. Neri and Barduccio pored over the illuminated text with appreciative eyes. It was a copy of Ovid's poems. Francesco and Stefano, on the other hand, were more pleased with the tapestry from Flanders which decorated the wall and portrayed the Queen of Sheba before Solomon. And while they admired these things, together with a painting by Lippo Memmi and a pair of silver candlesticks of delicate workmanship, there came a sound of men's voices below and three visitors abruptly entered the room.

One of them, called Tommaso, had been well known to Francesco Malavolti in his ribald days. But though the latter greeted him coldly, Tommaso —somewhat flushed with wine—thrust him in the ribs with coarse friendliness.

"Well, I see my friends and I have stepped into a nest of Caterinati!" he laughed. "And I am glad, for I would learn from you if it is true she goes hence to heal the great rift and stand the Antipope upon his head."

Before Francesco could reply, one of the other newcomers said roughly, "Heal the rift? Why,

Caterina caused it by dragging the Papal See from Avignon! I tell you that little scrap of a woman had best interfere no further. Let her stay at home and bake bread for her old mother and jaunt no more up and down the land."

Icily quiet, Neri fronted the speaker. "Is this your opinion, sir, or do you quote another?"

Belligerently the other cried: "What I say is said by everybody—except you few fools who hang upon her skirts. What good hath this Mantellata done except make other women discontent to stay at home and serve? She doth ill to rush to Rome!"

"Silence!" roared Francesco. "You speak of one set apart from all others by a holiness not of this earth."

"Holiness?" repeated the one called Tommaso. "Is it holy to make herself a mark for all eyes in Italy—with dozens of young men in her train, handsome youths like Maconi here?"

Stefano, his face white as chalk, towered over the drunken nobleman. "Had I not abandoned my old life and my trusty sword, you would not live to hear the echo of those words."

With a quick movement, Nanni di Ser Vanni pulled a cord against the wall and the sound of a bell jangled through his deep-toned speech. "Out of my house! You shame me, all three of you! Go defile the altar of the Duomo if you must be beasts, but say no word against this maiden of Siena or you will rue the day."

Two servants with scared faces came running in and flung wide the door. But Tommaso squared his chest. "We'll not go on that insult. Why care you, Nanni, if we laugh with all the city at this pretentious little creature—friend of popes—*you* once admired beauty in a woman!"

Francesco with a powerful arm collared the man and whirled him toward the door. There followed a confused struggle in which the intruders shouted curses and resisted the efforts of host and servants to force them out. At last, hearing a final offensive phrase hurled at Catherine's name, Ser Vanni in a fury whipped out his sword. "Take that, vile wretch!" he shouted and struck out at Tommaso with all his might. The blow was fierce enough to split the head of an ox.

But it never fell. Barduccio had leaped and caught that arm from behind. "Nay!" he cried. "No son of our sweetest Mamma may shed blood!" In the frightened silence which descended upon the man so narrowly delivered from death and upon them all, the boy added with the look of an avenging angel, "Go now, gentlemen, in peace and repent these falsehoods you have spoken of the greatest lover of beauty and of truth whom you shall ever know!"

Without another word the three contestants turned and followed the page down the stairs. In the street a small crowd had gathered to learn the cause of so much commotion. Apparently the scene was recounted by the three companions, for up through the starlit darkness came the oft-repeated derisive shout, "Caterinati! Caterinati!"

"Yes, by the grace of God," said Ser Vanni mop-

ping his brow, "that we are." Then turning to
Barduccio, he cried: "I thank thee, my boy, for thy
quick act. The devil leaped to my heart." He
snapped his sword back into its sheath and added
dryly, "I doubt, truly, if our most benign Mamma
would approve the killing of a man for her sweet
sake but, *per Dio*, he did well deserve death!"

Although before they parted the five friends
vowed never to speak of this outrage, Catherine was
fully conscious of what was being said anent her
wish to obey Urban's command. Even many of the
Mantellate echoed the general criticism. Such
hostile talk disturbed her and she wondered whether
she was injuring the cause of righteousness by so
fearless and so free a life. Perhaps, she thought, the
Bachelor was right to say the unvexed way of contemplation was best. For the first time in her life
she hesitated and finally wrote of her reluctance to
Fra Raimondo and the reason for it.

Although I am personally convinced that I am not
blameworthy on this point, for each time I set out it was
to obey God and His representative and for the salvation
of souls, I do not wish to be, through deliberate purpose,
a subject of scandal for any reason and therefore cannot
resolve to leave. But if the Vicar of Christ wishes absolutely that I come, then let his will be accomplished and
not mine.

As quickly as messenger could speed from Rome
the response came back. Categorically Urban Sixth
demanded that Catherine come to him at once. She
was quite ready and by mid-November was on her
way. With her went four faithful Mantellate, Fra

Bartolommeo, Father Tantucci, Neri, Barduccio, Gabriele Piccolomini, and Fra Santi who had loaned her his hermitage. Many others would have gone had she permitted.

No parting from her experienced by those who had to stay behind had ever been like that parting. For every reason—especially because of the peculiar closeness among members of the Fellowship during the last weeks—it was like heartbreak. Stefano and Matteo Cenni, Cristofano di Gano and a dozen others walked with the pilgrims to the Porta Romana. But none could jest about the *Bella Brigata* and its adventures. In the first place, their destiny seemed now to consist in facing a yawning chasm which no devotion could bridge and in the second place Catherine had never appeared so frail or so worn by suffering.

Those who rode with her observed that, as if imprinting them forever on her memory, she glanced back again and again at the receding towers and campanili of Siena. They saw her shade her eyes for a straining look at Belcaro's distant height. But from that moment on she was like a warrior whose bright lance is set for the charge and in her eyes was the mettlesome zest of battle. Her strength outlasted that of her companions and when they stopped wearily at Montepulciano she was fresh and ready to meet the needs of a friend at the convent there.

Such spirit was infectious. The little company sang along the way and exchanged with occasional wayfarers greetings of great cheer. When, at last, the bulky shape of Rome with its seven hills appeared, they were invaded by a feeling of excitement that was almost exaltation.

Pointing out the vast cylindrical outline of the Castello di Sant' Angelo, Neri murmured to Barduccio, "That fortress is the one they say was a great emperor's tomb."

Once within the formidable gates, the travellers were met by an escort and conducted to the appointed destination. There Fra Raimondo da Capua was waiting for them and none who watched Catherine greeting him did so unmoved. She clasped his hand with the look of a dry and thirsty plant watered at last by rain. That had been a separation of more than a year—twelve months of change and struggle, of small triumph, great defeat.

Near the foot of the Pincian hill the house assigned the group was prepared for their reception and fortunately, with their few possessions, settling was a brief business. For before two days had passed Catherine received notice of an appointment at Santa Maria in Trastevere where the Pope now resided.

Fra Bartolommeo, his own encounter still fresh in mind, was half afraid that Urban, despite his urgent summons, would show Catherine frosty rudeness. Even Fra Raimondo was a little nervous as he led his charge up the steps, down many corridors of the Papal mansion and into the audience hall. Indeed, that ponderous figure in white cassock and ermine-bordered cape, seated on the throne and surrounded by his Cardinals, presented a grim picture of Pontifical authority.

As she made her first genuflexion at the entrance of the huge room, Catherine observed a gentleman in the act of bowing himself out. Parti-coloured stockings and a doublet sewn with pearls gave him a lordly air. But his face, vaguely familiar to her glance, was distorted by a grimace of humiliated vanity. Evidently he had just been treated to a sample of the notorious Papal temper. She had time to notice that this individual, after a quick stare in her direction, did not leave the room, but instead paused near the door as if to judge whether she would fare better. Then she went forward, knelt again and finally reached the throne.

It was that lingering observer who wrote a pertinent comment on Catherine's first interview with Urban Sixth. He was a citizen of Siena and in a letter reporting to his government his transaction at the Holy See he said:

Caterina di Monna Lapa has arrived here and our Lord, Messer the Pope has seen her and heard her with pleasure; but what he asked of her is not known; it is only known that he received her with joy.

It was, indeed, a look of jubilant welcome that Catherine's lifted eyes found on the rugged face. The Pontiff bade her speak and as she did so he leaned upon the hands clasped in his lap with every air of profound attention. This time, of course, she needed no interpreter and the loving ardour, the passionate conviction of her phrases made their direct appeal.

When she had finished speaking, Urban, with cordial informality, turned upon his Cardinals a look of amazed triumph. "This little woman puts us all to shame!" he cried. "We are afraid and alarmed while she, who belongs by nature to the weak sex, feels no fear and even encourages us."

He questioned her a little and her replies caused a fresh outbreak of his enthusiasm. "What can the Vicar of Christ fear when the all-powerful Christ is with him? Christ is stronger than the world and it is impossible that he should betray His Holy Church!"

The interview had been long protracted before the Pope divulged his plan for the use of Catherine's genius. He wished her to go on a mission to Naples and persuade Queen Giovanna to cease battling against him. He proposed that the Mantellata go in company with a woman then in Rome who knew Naples thoroughly and was the daughter of a princess and a saint. This candidate was Karin of Vadstena, whose mother, Bridget of Sweden had laboured hard but vainly, to have the Avignon Popes return to Rome.

Such a plan was welcomed by Catherine with the utmost joy. Not only was it glorious to be trusted with a mission which meant changing enemy into friend, but she had always yearned over the beautiful and wicked Queen and longed to save her. Instantly she promised Urban she would go and he gave commands that Karin be sought out and presented with the urgent request.

This was promptly done and Fra Raimondo was acquainted with the result. When he went to tell Catherine what he had heard, however, his face was grave. "Dost thou know the story of what happened to Karin's brother when seven years ago Princess Bridget was at the Court of Naples?"

Catherine nodded impatiently. "I know, Father, and the Queen did wickedly to tempt the boy to an intrigue of love. She hath been possessed by the illusion of the senses. The young man's death was his salvation. All this is known to me. Yet if the Queen's heart did but change there would be rejoicing in both heaven and earth, and the Holy Father's cause would be greatly strengthened by an alliance with Giovanna."

Fra Raimondo shook his head. "This mission is not possible, my daughter. Karin doth refuse. She hates the Queen and Naples and is certain that for you both to go there would be to meet a vengeance which would stop at nothing shameful and cruel. The Swedish lady turns pale at the idea and will have none of it."

"Then I shall go alone!" Catherine sprang to her feet and her great eyes glowed with evangelical passion.

Her confessor looked at her with admiration and protested no more. But next morning he went privately to the Pope, told him all the tale and begged him to forbid Catherine's undertaking. After some dissension, Urban finally admitted the wisdom of this advice and forthwith sent word that the Mantellata was to remain in Rome.

When delle Vigne brought her that decision, Catherine raised her clasped hands in a fine contempt for caution. "If Agnes, Margaret, Catherine and the others had been equally afraid, they never would have won the martyr's crown. Have not all wise virgins a powerful Bridegroom to defend and protect them? Such hesitations prove rather lack of faith than prudent virtue!"

Great as was this disappointment, however, it was nothing compared to the loss she had next to sustain. The day after the *Brigata's* arrival Urban issued a bull of excommunication against the Cardinals who had elected Clement Seventh. His subsequent plan was to win over Naples and attempt negotiations with France. The ambassador he chose for the latter country was no less a person than Raimondo da Capua himself.

When that news came to the little house near the Pincian hill the *sala* echoed with the felicitations offered by the family to their distinguished comrade. Catherine led the applause. But as Fra Raimondo launched upon his plan to proceed by ship to Pisa and Genoa and thence by land to France, Neri chanced to glance at her face. The stark tragedy written on it shocked him. He thought: "It crushes her to lose him again so soon! Yet she says no word except of joy and pride."

Indeed, at that moment Catherine was feeling a

premonitory bereavement that affected her like a sudden illness. She still had so many matters to discuss with her confessor—her *Dialogues*, for example, she had barely mentioned. Moreover, she wanted his advice continually in dealing with Urban's temperamental difficulties. Almost at once, however, she was accusing herself of egotism to set her need against that of the Holy Church and before Fra Raimondo had been talking long, she leaned forward to listen with a smile.

Until his last moment on earth delle Vigne never forgot that day of separation. Just before he took the galley which was to bear him to the sea, he had two hours of talk with Catherine. Seated beside him in a secluded corner of the *sala*, she would sometimes lean over in the midst of a phrase, catch up his hand and holding it between her own, give him a look of deep trust and affection.

"Go and do God's work," she said at last and stood up. With a final tender smile she added in a tremulous tone, "I believe that in this life we shall never talk so long together as we have just done."

The Prior fixed his eyes upon the face he knew so well and with suffocating heart pushed from him the suggestion that this might be a last farewell. He was glad when she said she would walk with him to the river where the galley waited. In the courtyard all the family was gathered to bid him Godspeed, but none followed them when he and Catherine walked together over the rough streets.

One more hand-clasp before he stepped into the

boat! On the bank she waited to watch and smile. But when, with a great splash of oars the galley slid into the current of the muddy Tiber, she sank upon her knees and the tears came flooding down. Summoning her last ounce of strength, she made the sign of the Cross upon the foggy air and Raimondo's straining eyes saw that her lips moved.

"May God protect you, oh, my son!" she cried inaudibly, "but on this earth thou wilt never see again your little Mamma who so dearly loves thee!"

It was only the fishermen along the river and a passing Franciscan monk who witnessed that anguish, however. Her little circle was conscious of nothing but Catherine's renewed intensity for Urban's cause. Besides her many interviews with him she persuaded him partly by frequent letters to a plan which she framed to a double end. This was to gather about the Papal seat "a little company of saints"—men of holy life dwelling in various parts of Italy. Their presence would not only signify to all that the weight of goodness was on Urban's side of the Schism, but such an influence might prove a leaven to his nature. Already she divined with sinking heart the latent ferocity which later was to make this Pontiff's name a by-word. To this plan he amicably consented and Catherine both suggested most of the names and wrote letters adding her persuasion to Urban's command.

The hermits of Lecceto and of Spoleto, Don Giovanni of the Cells, the Prior of Gorgona and many more were summoned. Catherine also wrote

Stefano Maconi and told him there was need of him.

The bodies of those glorious martyrs are buried here in Rome, but their blood, which they shed with such fire of love in giving their lives for Life, their blood boils up, inviting you and the others to come and endure for the glory of God and Holy Church.

Neri, to whom she was dictating this message, said in a troubled voice: "Stefano has already sent two letters filled with desire to be near you and aid this work. It is his mother who holds him back from coming and he fears to wound her."

"*Oimè!*" Catherine stretched out her arms. "From the Colosseum to Saint Peter's Christians once died; outside the walls they lived like moles beneath the earth—all to preserve the Truth for us. Shall weakness prevent our serving a Church built on such foundations?" A heavy sigh escaped her. Then in another tone she said briskly, "And now a letter to Father Raimondo which shall reach him at Pisa and strengthen his heart!"

Would the Fellowship be strong for these great tests? That was what she asked herself and on Christmas eve she sent her overflowing love to each in prayer. On the morrow Neri found her singing as she worked at a little task of Christmas cheer. She was gilding the last of a basket of oranges.

"These are my small gift for the Holy Father," she cried looking up happily, "and thou must write a letter for me to go with it."

Delighted with this charming interlude in her

austere life, Neri touched the fruit with his slim finger. *"Molta bella, Mamma mia!"* he said smiling.

New Year's morning, dawning in a great ringing of bells, found Catherine wondering what 1379 would bring to the world. She felt ill. In terror she faced a sudden clear glimpse of exactly what would inevitably come—disappointment, confusion, strife, despair. But even as her heart contracted, the perspective changed, expanded. All this evil meant but the remaking of the Church which for its great mission needed a new structure on the old foundations. Time was nothing, Love everything and mankind was on its blind, slow, suffering way toward a heritage of Divinity—such was the light that all at once flooded the dark and stormy present.

Rising from her knees, she ran with quick feet down the stairs to greet the assembled household. "Good day, dear children! A glorious augury is ours—*ecco*, the sun is out!"

"Si, si," cried Barduccio in his clear young voice. "Let us give him proper salutation!" And he began to repeat for them the magnificent "Canticle to the Sun" which San Francesco had composed more than a hundred years before.

"O most high, almighty, good Lord God, to Thee belong praise, glory, honour and all blessing!

"Praised be my Lord God for all His creatures; and especially for our brother the Sun, who brings us the day, and who brings us the light; fair is he, and shining with a very great splendour. O Lord, he signifies to us—Thee!"

In the silence that followed the recitation, the little company looked at Catherine with one question in their hearts. What new climax of greatness would she attain in the next twelve months? To them the future was impenetrable, and no less so was the answer when it came.

Chapter Ten

THERE! Behold! Said I not this is the finest view of Rome?"

Neri, clasping his cloak tight against the January wind, turned exultingly to his friend Barduccio. The two young men had escorted Catherine and Fra Santi to the Papal residence in the Trastevere where she had been summoned for an interview. But, since their services were no longer needed, they had mounted the steep slope some distance behind the church of Santa Maria.

"Oh, *bella, bella vista!*" exclaimed the younger man and his delighted eyes dwelt upon the scene before them.

The afternoon, although cold, was clear as crystal. The tawny river caught glints from turquoise skies and beyond it, mellow as old parchment, stretched the Eternal City. Within the curve of the Aurelian wall were crowded those mediæval towers and narrow, tile-roofed houses of that age. But amidst them here and there rose the imposing shape of a triumphal arch and jagged outline of vast ruins—majestic structural spectres of a Rome which had ruled the world a thousand years before. Even the crescent Alban hills circling the sunny distance looked less old.

"Yes, it is beautiful from this point," mused Neri. "Farthest to the left by the northern wall is Monte Pincio below which we live and farthest to the right is San Giovanni in Laterano where stood the palace of the Popes before it burned. The monstrous broken bowl is the Colosseo."

"Its look is cruel," murmured Barduccio and turned his head. "I see the Rotondo plainly now. *Oimè*—albeit it is dedicated to all the martyred Saints, I, worthless one, like also to remember that beneath the great dome once were buried the rulers of a mighty empire." The two classicists exchanged a guilty look of sympathy. Then, again shifting the direction of his glance, the boy asked eagerly, "That hill between us and the Colosseo, near the height where we see the Palace of the Senators—did ancient Romans live there, thinkest thou?"

"Truly I know not," answered Neri. "They call that mount the Palatino. Only monasteries and castles and wild gardens are there now. Below it lies the Campo Vaccino where one day we saw the wild buffaloes grazing amid the waste. Often do I wonder about the past. Where did the Romans meet to make their laws, celebrate their victories, worship their gods? No trace remains to show us. Earthquake, fire and wars have left us little. I grieve for that."

"Besides," added the young Florentine, "that scholar told us here that many Christian churches are built with stones and pillars and marbles from pagan temples. There's one, however—look it's there near the bank across the river opposite—that little round temple, still undestroyed!"

"At least," went on the other, "we know where the Ancients went to bathe." He indicated the gigantic silhouette of the Baths of Diocletian to the north and, with a swing of his arm, the ruined Baths of Trajan.

They both fell silent, brooding over the panorama. "Come," Neri laid a hand on his friend's arm, "we must go back to the city. I always think how Pope Gregory at Avignon called it sad. It is, but not up here." He took a last glance at the sunlit scene and sighed a wish which was to take five hundred years for its fulfilment, "Roma, Roma, thou must some day yield up thy secrets to the world!"

That was an afternoon they long remembered. But, although they had little time for speculation on bygone, buried glories, these young scribes had no wish for days less crowded. The interest of the present was all-rewarding, even when anxious mo-

ments were upon them. What they could not understand was the hesitation of their fellows to come
and share the glorious struggle.

Nor, indeed, could Catherine. As January, 1379,
came to an end she began to feel that even her near-
est and dearest had shirked his place in line. Delle
Vigne wrote that when he had got as far toward
France as the border on the coast he and his companions had been warned that the party of the Antipope, the Clementists, had prepared an ambush for
them and that they had turned back. He was now
installed at Genoa and there would preach and
work for the cause of Urban Sixth.

Such pusillanimous retreat filled Catherine's
fiery soul with shame. "Thou art not worthy yet of
fighting on the field of battle," she wrote him
sternly. "Thou hast been left behind like a child,
hast fled danger and art pleased about it. Oh, wicked
father, what happiness for thy soul and mine if
with thy blood thou hadst cemented one stone of
Holy Church!"

But eagerness even for self-sacrifice, to say nothing of martyrdom, seemed to be her exclusive possession. Now arrived a letter from Brother William
Flete refusing absolutely to come to Rome. Although he had been named directly in Urban's bull,
he neither replied to him nor asked his permission
to remain in Lecceto, but simply announced to
Catherine that he could not leave his hermitage.

This was the sentimentalist who had kissed the
hem of her garment! Catherine rolled up the letter
and put it away in the small chest in her room.

When Neri asked her if she was not going to answer it, she lifted a face of ashes and wordlessly shook her head. Later, however, she wrote Father Antonio at Lecceto and told him what she thought of the Englishman's behaviour.

He says also that if you and the others came, you would lose your life of the spirit and so you would not be able to help with prayer nor remain in spirit with the Holy Father. Too lightly is the spirit held if it is lost through change of place! Is God then an acceptor of places, found only in the wood and not elsewhere in time of necessity?

Nor would Stefano Maconi heed her call. True, in order to be nearer the unworldly life and his friend Matteo Cenni, he had given up the luxury of his home and had taken a room in the Misericordia. From there he wrote letters brimming with love and loneliness, but also with excuses for not leaving Siena. Likewise, another of Catherine's disciples at home not only declined to join her, as she requested, but even failed to write. Just at this time, furthermore, the Abbot who had dedicated the Mantellata's convent at Belcaro and had stood always for devotion to the Church, lost his spiritual balance, came to Rome on a mission antagonistic to the Pope and was imprisoned.

Such sensational failures on the part of her friends constituted a bitter cup for Catherine to drink. Unwillingly she realized that the wisdom, the imagination and the force necessary to support Urban had to issue from the single source of her own being. In this sense she stood absolutely alone.

Yet, although the members of her household

looked to her for everything they did and thought, she would have been bereft without their love. In their gracious company she could fling off the weight of her responsibilities and enjoy innocent gaiety. Their good-humoured banter of Monna Lapa, who had recently journeyed from Siena to join them, always gave her great delight.

One dreary evening in February, as if blown through the door by the blustering wind, Father Tantucci strode into the *sala*. "Grandmother," he cried bluffly to old Lapa, "is not the supper ready? I do confess to an ache and hollow in my middle. I have been escorting strangers about the town all afternoon."

No wonder the friar was hungry and tired. It was enough to weary a man of steel to tramp those forlorn lanes. Because of the long period of neglect when the Papal See was at Avignon, the city offered little of the beauty developing so fast in Florence, Siena and Perugia. It lacked good paving, public buildings, fine palaces. The repair of the great churches, so well begun by Urban Fifth, had advanced but slowly. Worse than all else was the sullen unrest prevailing everywhere—intensified by the constant fighting around the Castello di Sant' Angelo. This fort was held by soldiers and followers of Clement Seventh and was besieged by citizens and Papal troops. Shocking scenes went on there every day. For if any one of the enemy fell into Roman hands, he was lucky to be merely slain and cries of tortured and mutilated captives continually filled the shrinking air.

To escape from these streets into the warm peace of their little house was to every member of the Fellowship like leaving hell for Paradise. Already this evening they were all gathered in the *sala* amid a hum of talk. Catherine, beside a small table on which stood a candle, was darning her worn, black mantle. She looked up gaily at Father Tantucci's question and waited in amusement for her mother's answer.

It came in the expected tone of grumbling affection, "What impatience!" cried Monna Lapa. "Dost thou not smell the good soup, my son? Today a friend whom Alessa hath made here brought us a basket heaping with good vegetables, and soon thy stomach will groan for a different reason than hunger."

"*Buona!*" laughed the Master. "Vegetables are the friars' meat."

At that moment Cecca Gori waddled in, supporting a pile of earthen bowls which towered to her chin. Behind her Alessa and Lisa brought to the hearth a great copper kettle and swiftly ladled out the steaming soup. When Cecca had placed the filled bowls in two rows upon the long table and a wooden spoon for each, the feast was ready and the men, who ate first, seated themselves in haste.

Hardly had Father Bartolommeo said the Grace, when Gabriele Piccolomini wailed in mock despair, "But, dear mother Cecca, where is the bread?"

"What? Is there none?" Cecca stood aghast. "Oh, by the blessed Saints today I forgot to buy the flour and now all the shops where loaves are sold will be shut fast. *Mea culpa*, little Mamma! Badly have I performed my duties for these hungry children."

Catherine had put aside her mending and was ready to read the Scriptures during supper. "Go and look," she said equably, "perchance the cupboard will yet yield something."

There was no denying that she, who scurried off upon her search, had to assume the blame. Catherine had so divided the housekeeping that each of the women was responsible for it one week at a time and this was Cecca's turn. Regretfully she came back with a plate of crusts and bits of bread—all the larder would yield.

Catherine had now disappeared and in her absence Alessa read the lesson. At last, rising from their seats, the men declared their hunger well satisfied and remarked with surprise that not a little bread remained uneaten. Indeed, even after the women had supped there was a residue of fragments. Wonderingly they looked at each other. Had there been more bread than they had realized? Or did the Holy Word supply that need of nourishment?

Lisa, however, had another explanation. "It is like the barrel of oil in thy house, Mother Lapa, which though empty continued to yield," she cried in a tone of awe. "Our little Mamma has been praying for us in her room. It is a miracle!"

No one questioned Lisa's interpretation. Yet to most of the group this instance of Catherine's inspired power was insignificant compared to an ac-

tivity which now made her known throughout all
Rome. A great crisis was facing both Papacy and
city. There had always been threat of it from the
Clementists within the walls and those besieged in
the great fortress which was once Hadrian's tomb
still proved impossible to conquer. Early in April
came news that made it likely these enemies would
receive outside support—Clement's troops were
marching against Rome.

For Catherine to hear that was to flame with a
fervour of defence in which love of the Church and
love of country blended. This army of the Antipope
was a band of Frenchmen! Never must they be
allowed to triumph. She hastened across the old
Pons Ælius near the Castello and on to Santa Maria
in Trastevere to hold audience with the Pope. Inspired by trained knowledge of affairs and quick
decisiveness, she had framed a plan of action. What
she urged was that Urban's soldiers be placed under
the absolute command of a skilled and brave captain
already in the Papal service. His name was Alberigo
Barbiano and before this Catherine had written him
a letter designed to inspire and dignify his purpose
as a battle of the Holy Cross. The Pope, at his wit's
end for wise counsel, accepted the idea and Alberigo
accepted the responsibility.

On the thirtieth of April near Marino in the
Alban hills the two forces met. Urban's *condottiero*
carried everything before him; won a complete victory and made prisoner three of Clement's leaders.
Meanwhile a last struggle was staged within the
city. Between a final bold assault upon Sant' Angelo

and bold negotiations undertaken by a Roman senator with the besieged, the stronghold capitulated and its menacing towers were destroyed.

That occasion when the conquering army returned and Rome was free of enemies became historic. Catherine and the Fellowship placed themselves on a balcony above the surging crowds to watch the troops march in. These bore a banner inscribed in letters of gold, "Italy, Liberated from Barbarians!" It was the first time a national army had been assembled, the first victory by Italians against foreigners.

When her eyes fell upon that proud emblem, Catherine said within herself, "This is the Crusade, at last!"

Yes, this was the Crusade—not the one for which she had worked and prayed against the infidels of the East, but a Crusade against the unfaithful of Europe and those aggressors who would destroy Italy with the Church. That her influence and energy had been instrumental in this first success had slowly filtered through diverse levels of Roman consciousness until it reached the populace. That glorious day they cried her name to the skies a hundred times. Leaning from her balcony with those grateful plaudits in her ears, straining her eyes for a last look at that golden word "Italia," Catherine felt the desolate sense of failure which had so long frozen her heart melt in the glow of thanksgiving.

As for those privileged persons who could be there beside her, their joy and excitement were boundless. Even the melancholy Neri was elated.

When the cavalcades of soldiers had nearly passed, he caught Barduccio's arm, crying, "*Ecco!* The Holy Father and his Cardinals and Bishops are coming now!"

Over the receding blare of military trumpets could be heard in the distance the sound of men's voices lifted in the sonorous cadence of the *Te Deum.* Far down the street sunlight splashed on the gorgeous yellows, reds and purples of priestly robes. From Santa Maria in Trastevere, the Pope was marching with all the Sacred College and the priests and Orders of the Church back to the Vatican. Rome was his now and the victory complete.

Monna Lapa craned her neck for this first glimpse of the Pontiff. And when she saw him she cried out joyously, "See, see in what way the Holy Father doth approach! After this who can say that he is proud?"

Quickly Fra Bartolommeo replied, "It was not he, but our most benign Mamma who knew the rightness of this show of piety. She did persuade him to it."

Before the advance of that procession the people knelt and tossed olive branches in the street and blessed the name of the great Prince who, in the ancient tradition of holy pilgrimage, in token of humility preserved in the midst of triumph, came walking barefoot all the long, rough way. Not for six hundred years had such a thing been witnessed.

Despite her active part in that battle against the Bretons and the Antipope, Catherine thought continually and with compassion of all its victims.

"Take care of the wounded!" she wrote Alberigo, the captain, and of the Pope she begged mercy and generosity toward his enemies.

This tremendous event was succeeded in less than a fortnight by cheering news from Naples. Urban and his followers had feared the worst from that section, not alone because of Queen Giovanna's perverse enmity, but because Clement Seventh had moved down into the castle she had given him and was suing for assistance from Neapolitan arms. In May that danger suddenly receded.

The Bishop of Naples was an Urbanist and had the majority of people with him. On the occasion of a street fight between some of this party and the Clementists, the entire city rose in fury against the Antipope. Roaring through the narrow lanes with cries of "Death to Clement! Viva Urban!" the mob made ready to slay everyone who opposed the legal Pope. In terror Clement fled the kingdom.

That exit occurred on May thirteenth. Just a week before, Catherine had sent one of her several letters to Queen Giovanna. This time, she had concluded her persuasive words with a prediction that if the Queen's hostility to Urban continued, the royal subjects would revolt. Without question the fact that this prophecy came true influenced Giovanna to act in haste and on May eighteenth she sent an ambassador to Rome and swore allegiance to the Pontiff at Saint Peter's.

How happy was the outcome of this conversion, Catherine learned one morning at the Vatican. "Daughter," said Urban, raising his two fingers in blessing, "thou wilt share our joy to learn that the Antichrist hath left Italy altogether. He journeys toward Avignon and will likely be there the last of June. Thus is our land purged of this curse of God!"

No one in Rome could so completely share the Pope's relief and exultation as the Mantellata. All these weeks she had been sending into all parts of Europe flaming messages to fire religious conscience and now with greater hopefulness she laboured the harder. She wrote to the King of England and to Charles Fifth of France. She urged peace between Venice and the King of Hungary. "Take hold of the little bark of Holy Church," she told the latter, "and help to lead her to a port of peace and quiet." To the Cardinal of Padua, to Charles of Durazzo who was married to a niece of Queen Giovanna, to Bishop Angelo Correr, destined to become Pope Gregory XII, to heads of Orders, hermits, private persons she directed fervid appeals.

They represented her very life's blood. As summer drew on her look of fragility had become an emaciation so extreme that to her companions it seemed impossible she could accomplish what she did. Almost every moment she was in pain. Yet she kept her nightly vigil of prayer, spent the morning in dictating letters, went almost daily to the Vatican and in the afternoon received the innumerable visitors who made her house the centre of ecclesiastical politics in Rome. Sometimes from those conversations came new suggestions for winning support for Urban.

As early as February she had heard from Cristo-

fano di Gano good news of the popular attitude in
Siena. "There is no one in this city who does not
hold it certain that Urban is the true Pope." Such
was the notary's report and Stefano confirmed it
later. Therefore Catherine made bold to write not
only to Maconi, but to the Lord Governors asking
that soldiers and money be contributed by the city
for the Pope's use. Florence received from her a
similar request. Perugia was subjected to more intense pressure. For there Catherine's letters were
delivered in person by Neri di Landoccio.

It was a painful wrench for the young poet to
leave her. "I go in sadness, little Mamma," he
mourned. "Why must the way of duty be so full of
thorns?"

"Dear my son," she clasped his hands with deep
affection, "think not it costs me nothing to part
with thee. But we must close the door on self-will in
order to shut out all that is not God. We are one in
His love and are never separated. We are creatures
of His infinite mercy and children of His light."

Neri's quiet courage and his great understanding were balm to her heart when from Fra Raimondo came a second disappointment. Once more
the Pope urged his going to the King of France—
this time by way of Spain. Catherine had hoped
much from such a plan. But the cautious emissary,
still at Genoa, wrote to Urban that since Pedro de
Luna was in Spain as Legate of Clement Seventh,
two ambassadors from the true Pope had already
been imprisoned in that country and therefore he
saw no good in even setting out.

To discover in her beloved and admired confessor such utter limitations was more than Catherine could bear. She tried to spur him to greater vigour.

If you had kept faith, you would not have wavered so much, nor fallen in doubt of God and me. But like a faithful son, ready to obey, you would have gone and done what was possible. If you could not walk there, you would have crawled; if you could not go as a friar, you would have gone as a pilgrim; if you had no money, you would have begged your way there.

She would have done all those things—did do them every day—and she simply could not accept the fact that he had less courage than her own.

Everyone about her observed the debilitating effect of this disillusion. Barduccio found Alessa crying with anxiety one day. "The little Mamma's strength is ebbing," she sobbed. "She suffers dreadfully. Yet when anyone speaks of care or of a remedy she doth refuse to listen and says God has found her worthy to bear pain and tribulation."

After Neri's return, however, she seemed stronger. She often spent an hour walking with him beside the river to get in private his comment on the general situation. By this time the family had increased in numbers and was established in another house on the via di Papa near the Dominican convent of Santa Maria sopra Minerva where Fra Raimondo had been Prior. It was very near the Pantheon or Rotondo which Baruccio so admired. There in the deep shade of those Corinthian columns which rose like mighty trees from floor to ceiling of the porch, the Mantellata would have liked to linger on hot afternoons. But whenever she stopped upon the way she became so surrounded by eager folk who begged for her blessing or her prayers that she had to seek the most obscure streets for all her walks.

Almost every day she traversed the long distance to the Vatican across the river. By word of mouth and pen she was trying to surround the irascible Pontiff with gentleness and mercy. During the summer this was not so difficult. Since Marino near the Alban Lake and almost all the neighbouring fortresses had capitulated to his authority, everything seemed to be going well. Nevertheless, even opponents of Clement remained hostile to many temporal claims of the Church and elements of anarchy in Rome where leadership had long been lacking menaced every gain of peace. One of the great feudal nobles in the city had recently refused obedience to Papal edicts and Urban in fury threatened him with excommunication.

Furthermore, with Clement triumphantly ensconced in Avignon, the Schism was only at the beginning of its forty years of duration. This might have been foreseen from the farcical first attempt to decide officially between the two Pontiffs. Louis d'Anjou for Clement, and the King of Hungary— together with Charles of Durazzo—for Urban, met during the autumn, but only to cling the harder, each to his own candidate.

Urbanists declared that the Schism had been a revolt against the Pope's holy purpose of purification. Frenchmen then pointed out that Urban's new Cardinals were not notable for their virtues and that he was no longer zealous for reform. Italians could not deny that accusation. Nor could Catherine deny it and she pleaded with the Holy Father to sustain his efforts for true good.

Was there no one in the world who cared what happened, she would ask in despair? Sometimes as she stopped to pant for breath on the exhausting walk back from the Papal mansion, she felt as if all the weight of humanity's indifference lay upon her shoulders and bent her to the earth. On entering the house she would lift aloud a passionate prayer—prayers which were often written down by some one and preserved—to draw upon the Divine Power which alone gave her courage to go on.

Always that courage was refreshed. When once more the treacherous Queen Giovanna retracted her allegiance, Catherine immediately wished to take up the matter. One of the Papal secretaries came to acquaint her with the facts, and with Neri and the Master they held a mutual conference.

"I think that stupid and wicked Giovanna will end by losing her kingdom." Such was the secretary's opinion.

Father Tantucci fingered the silver cross that swung against his black robe. "Tell us how far she doth oppose the Holy Father."

"At first," replied the Vatican official, "the Queen lent her influence to the Clementists only in secret. But now she hath shamelessly begun an open persecution of the followers of Urban. These wear a red rose and all who are for the Antichrist wear a white rose and the kingdom is divided into two camps. Yet court balls and jousting matches go on just the same. That ruler is the Devil's own daughter."

Catherine, who had sat silent, now leaned forward and her meditative face came to life. "Let me make one more attempt upon her conscience!"

"Her conscience?" laughed the secretary. "Daughter, that was murdered with her first husband."

"I shall send some one to her directly from me," went on Catherine unheeding. "Would I myself might go. But my son Neri here shall represent me. He shall take a letter, plead the cause of Urban at that court, find some method of bringing the Queen to reason. We must not lose Naples!"

"Those very words were spoken by His Holiness today," agreed the emissary. "That kingdom is the one place in Italy allied with Clement, and Naples must be won. I believe we had best raise up an army and attack the forces of Giovanna. Let enough blood flow in the streets of her city and the Queen will see that she was wrong!"

"First let me try persuasion. It might save a human soul." Clasping her thin hands, Catherine bent a tremulous smile upon the secretary's face. "I shall send my ambassador at once. Will you tell the Holy Father that?"

Rising to take his leave, the official said, "That I will and if anyone could stir that black heart to holy desire, my daughter, it is thou!"

After he had gone Neri asked quickly, "To Naples, little Mamma?"

He tried to keep from his voice the pain and horror the idea gave him. To be exiled once more was bad enough and one look at Catherine's haggard face struck him with chill to think of quitting her side. But of all places, that disreputable court where people laughed at everything he loved! This was a sentence, indeed! Then in those great dark eyes raised to his he read such desire for the good of God, of the Church, of mankind, that he flung himself on his knees before her. "Send me! I shall do my best!" he cried and bent his head that she might not see his desolation.

Catherine felt no less than he that this parting meant the last sacrifice. She bade him good-bye with the dry-eyed calm of despair and was proud to see him bear himself so gallantly. His last gesture was to tap that spot over his aching heart where he carried the letter she had written to the Queen. He himself had penned it.

Alas, how does your heart not burst with grief to see your people divided because of you? One side wears the white rose and the other the red, one maintains the truth and the other a lie! Can you not see that they were all created by that most pure rose of the eternal will of God and recreated to Grace in that most ardent crimson rose of the Blood of Christ?

In the doorway Catherine exchanged a farewell look with the young poet—a look that told him that, whatever his doubts and moods of melancholy, two things on earth were sure, her trust and her affection. They were his lance and breastplate.

After Neri's departure Catherine seemed to find

it more than ever discouraging and wearisome to labour with Urban's vengeful temper. She and all the Fellowship dreaded some outbreak of hostility against the incalculable being who sat upon the Papal throne. Barduccio found it difficult to put cheer into the postscripts he tucked into Catherine's letters to Neri. Those menacing clouds which darkened all Christendom hung directly above the little house near the Rotonda.

In amazement he and the others read the letters coming from Siena. Obviously no one there had any conception of what labour and suffering the frail leader was giving to brace the rickety situation of the Church. Not a single individual thought what he might give, but only of what he might get. Indulgences which required special sessions with the Pope were freely asked for; letters from Catherine were unceasingly demanded.

Patiently she gave what she could. She was delighted when she heard that Andrea Vanni had been made Captain of the People at Siena. At once she sent him a beautiful letter in which she begged him to work for justice and warned him against pride. Likewise, Stefano, who had wounded her so deeply, received her congratulations for his fortunate escape from an adventure which had made him for a day a prisoner of the terrible and famous John Hawkwood. Even more triumphant was her change of attitude toward delle Vigne. Abandoning, at last, the austere standard for him which had proved too severe for his nature, she concentrated on all those noble qualities he did possess. "We have good news

of Brother Raimondo," she wrote to Neri, "he does well and works with ardour for Holy Church. He is Vicar of the province of Genoa and soon will take the title of Doctor of Theology."

Barduccio, who took most of this dictation now, pondered the tone of these missives. There was a ring in it strangely reminiscent of those last meetings of the Fellowship in Siena—a poignancy in the old affection suggesting something which rent his heart. Catherine wrote as if to comfort them. For what? Still more frightening was the quality of the smile she had for everyone around her. That was meant for solace, too.

Gabriele Piccolomini asked him point-blank one day, "Why doth our most gentle Mamma remain so much alone? We seldom see her now at the repast and her joyous mien has changed. She smiles, but she is sad."

Barduccio turned to stir the fire and as he did so a great tear splashed upon the hearth. "She desires that we should not see her pain," he choked. "She suffers in mind and body and only God can help her."

On New Year's eve the little family sat late to give each other cheer. Catherine was not with them, but they spoke only of her.

"Never since she began to serve the world," declared Fra Bartolommeo, "has she passed such a year. I cannot comprehend its terrible misfortunes."

"Before this time our dearest Mamma hath always had vast profit in work for peace," mourned the Master, "but now wickedness hath grown too great."

No one could bear to utter the word which stared blackly from the page of that past twelve months. Failure! It was incredible that she, so daring and triumphant, should not have achieved some impressive success. And what now? To what could she look forward? Always some glorious action had loomed ahead. But in whatever direction these faithful followers looked, they shuddered at the bleak, forbidding prospect. No more than they had understood what she had really accomplished in Rome could they foresee that the year 1380 was to bring her the greatest of all adventures.

On New Year's Day one of the Cardinals who greatly admired Catherine asked her to offer a special prayer for the Pope. In that supplication she uttered her unique desire—that she might, by sacrifice of body and even of eternal bliss, be the atonement for the evils which crushed the world. If there were just one bit of firmness anywhere! If she could only find something to make her say, "This, at least, is a fragment of goodness which will last!" But there was none. And no one was more uncertain than he who should have led the world. A tiger stalked behind the Papal throne. She felt his hot breath and anticipated his spring upon the innocent. It was not strange that Urban was a lonely figure. But how terrible that no heartfelt support for him—money, troops, enthusiastic devotion—could be relied upon in any part of Italy. Would Clement triumph and again make the Church a captive of France? Could it be true, as many thought, that this Schism had resulted from the Pope's return to Rome and was she, therefore, guilty of the rift? That bitter fruit was the only harvest of her labours.

Such were Catherine's thoughts about the world. To work with flaming passion for a cause and yet lay down her will and merely trust—this was her duty as she saw it. She must give everything, fail, suffer and yet be serenely confident that all was for the best. In anguish she strove to reach that inner goal.

There came a Sunday, the thirtieth of January, when she felt all the frantic demons of doubt tearing her to bits and in terror she dragged herself out to Saint Peter's to fling herself down at the Apostle's tomb and ponder on his martyrdom. He must have experienced this very agony and infinitely more. Oh, that he might show her how to be empty of every consciousness except love! Complete surrender—that was her desire.

Several Mantellate had gone with her to the church and they remained near and watched her anxiously. At last they saw the look of suffering disappear and that worn face light with marvellous felicity. Her burning eyes, her pale hands lifted before the grille in prayer, made her seem a flame—a flame that flickered in the scented dusk of the church.

Suddenly to the terror of those watchers it went out. Catherine had crumpled upon the tiles. The women tried to raise her. It seemed impossible. Her limbs were stiff and paralysed and that frail, small body had become heavy as if, indeed, it had received the weight of all human guilt. Only with the utmost difficulty could the Mantellate get her home.

For three days she lay in deathly stillness, but late in the afternoon of the fourth, she roused up energetically and sent for Barduccio. As if nothing had happened, she said to him with a smile, "My son, what news of the Holy Father?"

Transported that she was herself again, he told her that much had happened. An armed mob had broken into the Vatican and pushed as far as the audience chamber. There, dressed in robes of state, the Pope received them with unwonted calm, listened to their complaints and dismissed them in such a fashion that they went quietly away. "Thy spirit works upon him, dearest Mamma!" cried Barduccio triumphantly.

"I must prepare a letter to him," she answered. "Art thou ready?" Panting for breath, but with all her old vivacity she composed a message which would inspire Urban to deal gently with his rebellious subjects.

I beg of you, most Holy Father, that as you have begun so do you continue to confer often with them and prudently bind them with the bond of love. . . . I know that you must know the nature of your Roman children, that they are led and bound more by gentleness than by other force or harsh words; and you realize also how necessary it is for you and Holy Church to conserve this people obedient and reverent towards you; because here is the head and the beginning of our Faith. . . . And forgive me, sweetest and holiest Father, for saying this to you.

As she pronounced with an adoring smile the words which closed her every letter, "*Gesù dolce, Gesù amore*," she fell back unconscious.

Thoroughly frightened, Barduccio shouted for Cecca and Alessa and all bent over her. "Her limbs are rigid and she scarcely breathes," cried the boy. "Oh, dear my mothers, do not let her die!"

Next day she was much better and for a fortnight she pursued her programme of work and prayer as usual. The family decided that she was in the grip of some intense inner struggle which was merely reflected in her physical state. So, indeed, she was. It seemed to her she was intercepting all the hatred which streamed through the world and her experiences were so strange that instinctively she sent to delle Vigne, so long her confessor, a detailed description of them.

I seemed no longer in my body, but I saw my body as though it belonged to another . . . I could not move my tongue or any other member . . . I therefore left my body as it was and my intellect remained fixed on the abyss of the Trinity. . . . When they carried me upstairs my room seemed full of demons who began to wage another battle against me, the most terrible I ever endured, trying to make me believe and see that I was not she who was in the body, but rather an impure spirit. . . .

When it is the hour of terce I rise from Mass and you would see a dead woman go to Saint Peter's. . . . There I stay thus till near the hour of vespers and from this place I would depart neither day nor night until I see this people at least a little steadily established in peace with their Father. This body of mine remains without any food, without even a drop of water; in such sweet physical tortures as I never at any time endured; insomuch that my life hangs by a thread.

At this point the letter took on a tone of finality. She asked Fra Raimondo to "gather together in thy hands the book and any writing of mine that thou mayst find and do with them what thou seest will be most to the honour of God—things in which I found some recreation." She told him to look after her sons. "I promise to do more for them and for thee after my death than in my life." To forgive her sins and give her his blessing was her request. That he might labour zealously for the Holy Church was her affectionate council.

What did such a letter mean, Barduccio asked himself in terror. He saw Catherine walk to Saint Peter's every day until the last of February. She seemed only a little weaker. Then one day she could not move. Paralysis had returned and she was obliged to keep to that wooden plank she called her bed. Yet her smile was so gay, her voice so strong, that everyone thought the attack would pass off as so many previous ailments had vanished.

Suddenly—it was not till April had come with its sweet airs, not till the wistaria was in bloom over creamy old walls—the truth was upon them all. In vain, they tried to smile away their unbelief. The meaning of that excessive weakness which augmented day by day could no longer be denied. Those devoted men and women saw, inevitable as Time itself, an ultimate shadow draw ever closer to fold their beloved in its dark embrace. Catherine Benincasa was dying.

In haste Fra Santi sent for one of her great friends at the Vatican, the Pontifical Protonotary. When he reached her bedside he was so shocked by her look that he could not speak and in silence bent down to hear her comradely greeting. When he saw, however, how calm and happy, how perfectly aware and unafraid she was, he recovered his equilibrium.

"Mamma," he said with tender frankness, "it seems that thy Divine Bridegroom calls thee to Him. Hast thou thought of those last measures thou shouldst take before leaving?"

The marvellous, vivid eyes in that mask-like face sparkled with amusement. "What dispositions should I make?" she whispered. "A poor little woman like me who owns nothing at all?"

"Oh, thou canst leave a fine will if thou wouldst tell each one of thy disciples what he ought to do after thy death. I ask it in the love of God and am sure that all would obey thee even as I."

Delighted that she still might give something to her dear ones, she roused herself to dictate her final suggestions for the true way to live, and recommended to her sons and daughters how they should dispose of their remaining years.

As she finished speaking, she looked about the room and was surprised to find it full of people. Not only her close family, but many friends from all parts of Rome had heard the alarm and hastened to the via di Papa.

A few days later a hasty knock sounded on the door of the little house. Alessa, who had gone wearily to open it, fell back astounded to see who it was that entered. Spent, as if he had been riding night and day, fixing her with eyes of dread and compunction, Stefano Maconi stood before her.

After she had reassured him, he burst out: "I knew our sweetest Mamma was ill, but she has been ill so often and yet recovered and I knew not what to do. I went about Siena praying in all the churches and at last a voice bade me hasten here if I would see my blessed Mamma alive. At once I left. Oh, mother Alessa, will she know me?"

She knew him and talked with him, talked with them all. And not one left the room for long and Lapa, bowed with grief, never stirred from her post beside the bed. Thus they were gathered on Sunday, April twenty-ninth, just before the dawn. Through them all had thrilled the knowledge that the hour had come and the final rites had to be accomplished. Alessa gathered the beloved, wasted form into her soft arms and held her thus and never moved. The Pope's plenary indulgence was imparted, the last Sacraments administered, the anointing oil applied. All at once, as if again that demon visitation had come upon her, she struggled darkly, gasped for breath. After an hour of this, a luminous calm descended.

The change was startling. All the watchers leaned forward eagerly. For Catherine's eyes were full of life and joy. She had conquered the demons as she had conquered all other temptations and had gained the blissful surrender she had longed for. Now she could yield to happiness, to the prospect of a union, perfect where it had only been partial.

It was Life, not Death, which she felt approaching. "Master Tantucci," she whispered.

When he had pressed close to her, she made aloud the general confessional and asked all those present to forgive her many sins. She beckoned to Stefano and murmured in his ear a word for himself and a message for her dear, exiled Neri. Suddenly she asked for her mother's blessing and as Lapa gave it, bending down with choking sobs, there swept over the room anew the awful finality of this moment. This was the end of all their precious comradeship, their loving relation with a being whose like they would never meet again.

Now they understood what had bewildered them before. However Catherine had been checked by outer circumstance, she had triumphed spiritually and the earth was sure to blossom with the seeds her hand had sown. Down upon their knees went these men and women. They watched the dark glint of Catherine's eyes upon the Crucifix. They drank in her look of angelic bliss and, at last, they heard the faint breath of those words which Christ had uttered, "Father, into thy hands I commend my spirit."

Gently Alessa laid the empty body down. There was a moment's hush of realization. Then Stefano rushed downstairs and locked the outside door. When he returned, about that narrow bed and that still figure, the Fellowship held its last meeting. In the end, they could talk about her, glorify her, remember everything, but at first all their hearts could hold was tears.

For three days this exclusive concentration of grief and gratitude remained unbroken. Then at night Stefano was allowed the honour of carrying in his arms that light burden to the Church of Santa Maria sopra Minerva. Within a bier behind a grille at the left of the altar they placed the slender form clothed in its familiar white robe and shabby mantle. Barduccio and Stefano kept the watch. They knew as they knelt there and all the others, departed on last errands, knew that their moment of possessiveness was over. From then on she who had been their little Mamma belonged to the world.

By daylight the entire city was aware. Bells tolled in every church and pomp and ceremony took a hand in mourning. Pope Urban ordered a great Requiem to be sung. It was followed by another, even more magnificent, commanded by a Roman senator. But the tribute of Rome lay not in ceremonial. It was brought by the poor and humble folk, by simple priests and monks and children who streamed from dawn till dark into the church of the Dominicans. They paid their homage. They brought their sick for healing and knelt weeping at the shallow bier.

And all the narrow streets which wound from San Giovanni to the Vatican stirred with the magic whisper, sorrowful and exultant, the whisper which rose to a pæan ringing from Siena through all Italy and which at last was to reach the far corners of the earth. "She was a Saint! A Saint!"

Epilogue

"Dearest Brother:—

I believe you know that our most reverenced and dearest Mamma went away to Paradise on Sunday the 29th of April, praised be Our Saviour, Jesus Christ, Crucified and Blessed. It appears to me that I remain an orphan, since from her I had every consolation and I cannot keep myself from weeping. I do not weep for her, but I weep for myself who have lost so much. I could not have lost more and you know it. . . . I take comfort because you know she said that she would be better and more useful to us dead than living. Know, dearest brother and—may I say it—son, that when I can be in your presence much pain will diminish. . . .

Your servant, Nigi di Doccio, orphan. I greet you as I can."

THIS letter from one of Catherine's sons in Siena was written to Neri and he received it at Naples where he still strove to accomplish the impossible. Not long afterwards, however, he found himself free to leave

Giovanna's dreadful court and follow out Catherine's last words of advice to him by entering a retreat near Florence.

Stefano Maconi, also, lived only to obey those ultimate words which he had stooped to catch from the lips of his dying leader. Within a year he had entered the Carthusian Order as a monk. As for Fra Raimondo, he had just gone from Genoa to Pisa and then to Bologna for the general Chapter meeting of the Dominicans when the news of Catherine's death reached him. It was there he was elected head of his Order—an honour he would have been so proud to announce to her who had knelt weeping on the bank of the Tiber when destiny had swept him away.

It was three years before his duties brought him back to Rome—three years before he could visit that tomb at Santa Maria sopra Minerva. When he did so, however, it was with the determination to gratify the urgent wish of Siena to do honour to its glorious citizen. Therefore, he secured Pope Urban Sixth's permission to undertake that strange commission which the child-like literalness of adulation required in that age. What the Pope called "a pious dismemberment" was accomplished. Catherine's body was left in state in Rome, but the head was carried back as a sacred relic to the city of her birth. In secret it was brought to the San Lazarino Hospital where once Catherine had nursed the old leper. Meanwhile the great funeral ceremony was organized.

On May 5, 1383, the vast processional began.

From the Porta Romana to San Domenico all the people of Siena massed along the way. The heralds were two hundred little girls in white and two hundred little boys gorgeously dressed like pages—all bearing bouquets of blossoms and roses to strew the path for her who had so loved flowers. Behind them came all the corporations and representatives from each *contrada* amid a swirl of torches and brilliant banners, and next, the Confraternities with lighted candles in their hands and a great Crucifix borne ahead. Then followed the Friars and the Orders with the Dominicans in the place of honour and Abbots and Bishops in full panoply of mitres, jewels and trappings. At last, amid the choir, borne beneath a baldequin with censers swinging fragrant incense round it, came the bronze reliquary with the holy relic. All the bells pealed constantly and the procession passed down one endless lane of kneeling mourners.

Fra Raimondo, Fra Bartolommeo, Tommaso della Fonte and other priests who had known Catherine well marched in that procession. Messer Matteo Cenni, Cristofano di Gano, Stefano and Neri walked side by side. Already there were gaps in the ranks of the Fellowship. Alessa Saracini had died in Rome but a few months after her dearest friend, and Barduccio Canigiani within the year. But old Cecca and many other Mantellate were there to do their leader honour. Last of all came a little bent figure, with wrinkled, tear-stained face and eyes that gazed incredulously at all that majestic ceremonial of praise. It was Monna Lapa.

One Dominican in that group was to devote his whole life to the perpetuation of Catherine's name. He was Tommaso di Nacci Caffarini. Although he had known Catherine at Siena and had been with her at the Rocca, his diverse duties had prevented him from close membership in her circle. Yet no one in the Fellowship did so much as he to assemble documents and letters which preserved forever the marvellous details of that extraordinary career. Fra Raimondo, to be sure, undertook almost at once a biography of Catherine in Latin, but it was Caffarini who insisted that he finish it.

As the years went on the members of the Fellowship, almost without exception, proved themselves worthy of their great association. Delle Vigne, Caffarini and another Dominican named Bartolommeo da Ferrera became the most potent reformers of their day. Stefano Maconi rose swiftly in the Carthusian Order until he became its General. Even Francesco Malavolti finally made his contribution. After the death of his wife he became an Olivetan monk, increasingly trusted with responsibilities. Likewise, Cristofano di Gano, whose wife and children were carried off by another plague, became a Brother at the Santa Maria della Scala Hospital and at last its director. As for Neri, his hermit life of contemplation, lived first near Florence and then near Siena, did not prevent an ever increasing sphere of loving influence. Until his death he was the pivotal point of that widely scattered circle.

When Raimondo da Capua finally finished Catherine's life in Latin, Caffarini turned it over to Stefano Maconi for translation into Italian and never ceased to prod him until the task was done. It was called *The Legend* and many copies of it were made by devoted hands. Then Caffarini wrote a briefer version called *The Minor Legend* and added a supplement with further facts. Moreover, his constant praise of Catherine's name from his pulpit at Venice and the little plays he caused to be performed to illustrate the incidents of her life focused anew the attention of the Catholic world upon the Sienese Tertiary.

At last the Bishop of Venice instituted a process in which Caffarini and Bartolommeo da Ferrara were obliged to defend themselves against exalting a person uncanonized by decree. Immediately the two Dominicans saw their opportunity. They proceeded to collect all the material necessary to justify such canonization. Every living person who had known Catherine was requested to send in a written statement of all that individual's personal knowledge of the Mantellata—a statement duly sworn to before a notary. Because of this notable effort there remained for future generations, in addition to the life and the collected letters, a wealth of personal detail set down by contemporaries which has made Catherine Benincasa one of the best authenticated figures of her day.

Not until 1461, however, was this celebrated being assigned a place among the Saints of the Church. It was the privilege of a fellow citizen of hers, a member of the Piccolomini family of Siena, who had been elected Pope, to issue the Papal Bull of Canonization. In the sumptuous library of the Duomo one of the frescoes of Pinturrichio depicts this Pius Second presiding over the ceremony. Thus was fulfilled the dream of countless hundreds. The act of Pious Second set the sacred seal upon that realization of her more than earthly goodness which had spread from her followers to all who saw her, heard her, received her letters, read her life or had any knowledge of her whatsoever.

Every year on the 29th of April Siena holds a three-day celebration of its Saint. The tiny room where once she knelt through long vigils of pain and bliss and the Capella Volta at San Domenico where Andrea Vanni's portrait of her hangs above the altar are visited by pilgrims from many lands. Children sing her hymn in the streets and banners hang from every old house in the Contrada of the Goose. Flowers are massed within her votive chapel and by great cantatas, sermons and processionals the city demonstrates that now as vividly as five and a half centuries ago Catherine lives in the hearts of her people.

Moreover, even as during her life that personality draws to itself many of the most cultured individuals in Italy today. The Studi Cateriniani comprises a group of scholars who are constantly at work upon the period in which Catherine and her followers lived. New letters and new facts are continually being discovered and every aspect of her service to Church and State is exploited in the publications of the society and in frequent lectures. Constantly this interest widens beyond national boundaries and biographies of the Mantellata have been written in many languages. The great ideas and conceptions she expressed still serve as inspiration—patriotism, a unified and purified Church, peace, and a true self-knowledge. Furthermore, it remained for the present age, concerned as it is with feminine liberation, to appreciate in full the amazing example she offered in the fourteenth century.

Therefore, although by birth she belongs to Siena, by her patriotism to the Italian nation and by religion to the Catholic Church, Catherine Benincasa belongs by her great revelation of Divine Love to all humanity.

BIBLIOGRAPHY

A Cultural History of the Modern Age
     —Egon Friedell
A History of the Papacy   —M. Creighton
Avignon   —Thomas Okey
Avignon au Temps des Papes —Robert Brun
Come Vestivani Gli Uomini del "Decameron"
      —Carlo Merkel
Costumes de la Cour de Rome —P. Helyot
Dialogo di Santa Caterina da Siena
   —(Editor) P. Innocenzo Taurisano, O.P.
Epistolario di Santa Caterina
    —(Editor) Piero Misciattelli
From Rome to Florence —Hubbard Hutchinson
Guide to Siena   —W. Heywood
History of the Popes   —Ludwig Pastor
History of Siena   —E. D. Gardner
History of Siena   —Langton Douglas
How Music Grew   —Bauer and Peyser
I Fioretti di S. Caterina da Siena
    —P. Innocenzo Taurisano, O.P.
Il Sentimento di Patria nell Opera di S. Caterina
      —Pietro Rossi
I Sonetti   —Folgore da San Gemignano
Italicarum Rerum Scriptores (Chronicles of Siena)
      —Muratori
La Devota Revelazione O Dialogus Brevis
     —Francesco Valli
La Spirito, il Cuore, la Parola di Caterina da Siena
     —Niccolo Tommaso
La Mule du Pape   —Alphonse Daudet

Leggenda Maggiore
—RAIMONDO DELLE VIGNE DA CAPUA
Leggenda Minore —TOMMASO NACCI CAFFARINI
Les Papes d'Avignon —G. MOLLAT
Le Vesti delle Donne Fiorentine nel Quattrocento
—E. POLIDORI CALAMANDREI
Lives of the Popes in the Middle Ages —HORACEK
Mœurs, Usages et Costumes du Moyen Age
—PAUL LACROIX
Palio and Ponte —W. HEYWOOD
Processus Contestationum super Sanctitate et Doctrina B. Caterinae de Senis
Ricordi —CRISTOFANO DI GANO GUIDINI
Rime —PETRARCHA
Saint Catherine of Siena —ALICE CURTAYNE
Sainte Catherine de Sienne —JOHANNES JOERGENSEN
Sainte Catherine de Sienne —ALEXANDRE MASSARON
Saint Catherine of Siena as Seen in Her Letters
—VIDA SCUDDER
Storia della Pitture —G. B. CAVALCASSELE
Studi Cateriniani (Publication Series)
The Design and Development of Costume
—ADOLF ROSENBURG
The Disciple of a Saint —VIDA SCUDDER
The Ensamples of Fra Flippo —W. HEYWOOD
The Mystics of Siena —PIERO MISCIATTELLI
The Story of Siena —E. D. GARDNER
Vita del Beato Giovanni Colombini —FEO BELCARI
Vita di Santa Caterina da Siena
—P. LUDOVICO FERRETTI DEI PRED.

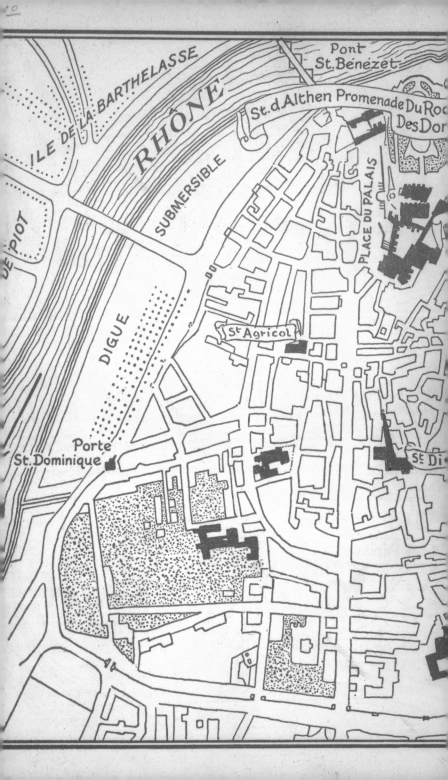